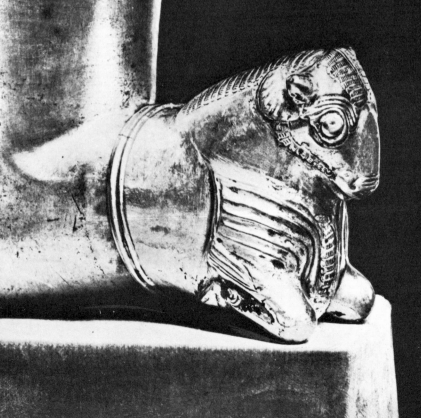

BULLS
THROUGH THE AGES

BULLS

LUTTERWORTH PRESS

THROUGH THE AGES

Ralph Whitlock

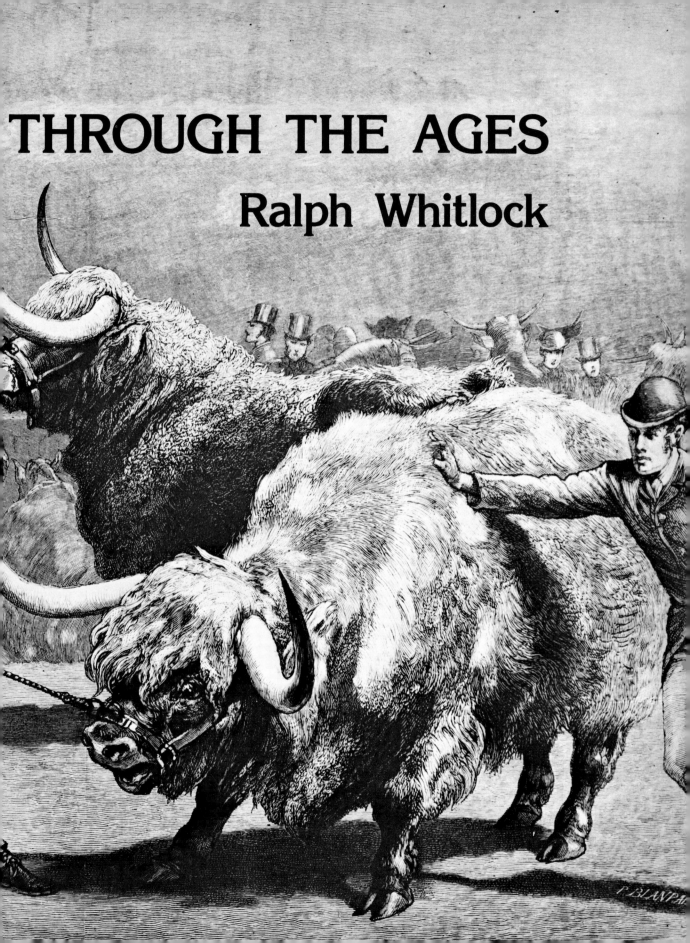

First published 1977

Acknowledgements

The author wishes to thank Professor H. C. Pawson for permission to quote from his book *A Survey of the Agriculture of Northumberland* on the subject of Chillingham Wild Cattle and the Librarian of the Zoological Society of London, Mr. Arthur Sutton of the *Birmingham Post*, and the staff of Yeovil Public Library for helpful assistance they gave so willingly.

The publishers are grateful to the following for permission to reproduce the photographs of which they hold the copyright:

Australian News and Information Service 152, 170; *A. Bishop* 157 (Limousin bull, owned by Major A. R. Trotter, Charterhall, Duns, Berwiskshire); *British Museum* Front cover, 43, 44; *Calgary Stampede and Exhibition* opp. 129; *Central Office of Information* 126, opp. 128 above and below, 130, opp. 145 above, 167, 168; *Bruce Coleman Limited* opp. 16, opp. 33, opp 81, opp. 112 above, opp. 161 below *Livestock Farming* 6, 9, opp. 160 below; *Mansell Collection* Half-title, Title page, 25, opp. 32, 34, 37, 52, 53, 55 left and right, 58, 61, opp. 65 above and below, 70, 73, opp. 80 below, 110, 134; *J. E. L. Mayes* 155; *Morgan-Wells Studio* opp. 112 below (Highland Bull owned by L. R. Derisley Esq., Byfleet, Surrey); *Musée de L'Homme, Paris* opp. 17; *Museum of English Rural Life* 12, 99, opp. 145 below, opp. 160 above; *Museum of London* 40; *Radio Times Hulton Picture Library* 15, 50, 56, 68, 69, 75, 76, opp. 80 above, 85, 86; *Rothamsted Collection* 11, 93, 107, opp. 113 above and below, 114, 115, 117, 118, 120; *Robert Harding Associates* opp. 64; *Staatliche Museen Berlin* 46; *Zoological Society of London* Back cover, 23, 27.

The illustration on the half-title shows a Hittite drinking-horn found in Anatolia, dating *c.* 7th century B.C.

The illustration on the title page is a John Charlton drawing of a cattle show, 1882.

ISBN 0 7188 2330 3

COPYRIGHT © RALPH WHITLOCK 1977

Filmset in Baskerville 169, 12 on 15pt: Quotes, 11 on 13pt: Captions, 11 on 13pt.

Printed Offset Litho in Great Britain by
Jolly & Barber Ltd, Rugby, Warwickshire.

Contents

1

The Fascination of Bulls

"In the Spring a livelier iris changes on the burnish'd dove;
In the Spring a young man's fancy lightly turns to thoughts of love."

The familiar lines express the truth that all living creatures reach their peak of attraction when ripe for reproduction. The maturity of their sexual organs is linked to what are termed secondary sexual characteristics, of which the antlers of stags, the flaunted iridescent feathers of peacocks, the dark, shaggy mane of the lion and the exaggerated tail-streamers of birds of paradise are examples. In a wider context, the brilliant hues of flowers and butterflies serve the same purpose. They are stimuli to reproduction, thus ensuring the continuance of the species.

Preparation for breeding with most vertebrate creatures follows the same pattern. With adrenalin coursing through the veins, the eyes of the male grow bright, movements more sprightly, behaviour aggressive. Determined to protect their females or the territory where their young are to be born, the males utter ringing challenges, strut boastfully and hold themselves in readiness to drive away all intruders. It is the natural role of the male.

Human reactions to courtship displays by animals vary. We take a delight in bird song, which to the birds is a challenge to rivals, yet seems to us merely the authentic voice of welcome spring. The brilliant colours of the cock pheasant and the rhythmic courtship dance of the great crested grebe strike us as being beautiful. We are not so sure about the bulbous nose of the sea elephant, which swells to twice its normal size in the mating season. And the mating behaviour of many of the larger mammals we tend to find somewhat alarming, because of their size and power. The roar of a lion

(Left) *In most of the great beef-producing countries of the world the white-faced Hereford is dominant.*

7

reverberating through the African night sends shivers up our spine. We admire the magnificent antlers of the red deer stag and are impressed by his pugnacious antics at rutting time, but instinct warns us to keep clear. Big bull elephants fighting for a female are a fearsome sight.

The bull is among the foremost in the category of alarming animals. He epitomizes masculinity and virility. He arouses in us primitive instincts – fear; the admiration of sheer animal power; the thrill of an expressed challenge.

In boyhood on an English farm, I was familiar with bulls from my earliest days. I knew a series of bulls by name, helped to rear some of them from calf-hood, and handled them daily. Yet even I was not immune from the spell when I met a semi-wild bull on a vast ranch in Texas. He was a huge red animal of the Santa Gertrudis breed. I became aware of his presence when, fascinated by the behaviour of some small birds called Pyrrhuloxia, I ventured on the wrong side of a six-stranded barbed wire fence, reinforced by cacti. He came at a trot from the far side of the pasture, where his harem was grazing, but fortunately I saw him in time and retreated hastily. Fortunately, too, the gate was both strong and negotiable. With me safely on the other side, he tested it with his horns, sending vibrations along the wire. He pawed at the ground, kicking up spurts of dust and uttering low moans of frustration. The thick hair on his humped shoulders bristled. He rolled his eyes menacingly, revealing their bloodshot whites. Saliva dripped from his mouth.

So we stood, staring at each other, and I knew that, but for that gate, I was looking at death. He would have enjoyed nothing better than killing me. In a recent book I have described heavy horses as "gentle giants", but there was nothing gentle about this giant. Those wide horns were for goring and tossing; those mighty shoulders could hurl me into the air and crush me when I fell. I was not so much an enemy as an intrusive nuisance – something to be stamped out of existence and then forgotten.

At that moment I thought that I could appreciate the thrill of bull-fighting. I could begin to imagine what it would be like, supposing I possessed the necessary skill, to enter an arena with that bull. I would be scared yet exhilarated. I would, standing close by those massive shoulders, thwart all his efforts to kill me, and at the end I would win. What a combat that would be!

My thoughts ran along those lines because, I suppose, he was such an obvious challenge. I was reacting in the same manner as a boxer who climbs into the ring with a formidable opponent, or as a mountaineer preparing to climb a difficult mountain. Why does a mountaineer match himself against Everest? Because it is there. The conventional answer, but one which reveals deep insight into the human spirit. To match oneself against a bull such as this, and to master him, would be a worthy achievement. (Happily, I do not have the necessary expertize!)

Herein lies much of the fascination of bulls. It is a purely instinctive reaction. Withdrawing from the immediate vicinity of this mighty animal and considering the matter objectively, I could appreciate that he was behaving in the normal manner of most breeding males. On the far side of the pasture he had a herd of females with their calves. He was their protector. It must be admitted that he was filling the role quite efficiently.

He was, in fact, a lucky animal. Comparatively few bulls can live a normal life today. Their very strength is their downfall. Only the strongest fences are adequate to keep such a sire as that Santa Gertrudis bull within bounds. And few farmers in overcrowded industrial countries are willing to take the risk. One gate left carelessly open by a rambler, and there is hell to pay. Consequently, most bulls in settled farming country are kept tied up or in small pens, emerging only for daily exercise in a yard or when they are called upon to serve a cow. It must be a frustrating life for

Frustrated by modern restrictions, a Hereford bull exercises in a yard.

such muscular and energetic animals – comparable, one would think, to a life sentence in a modern jail.

From the bull's viewpoint, the situation is not improved by the widespread adoption of the modern technique of artificial insemination. By this method one bull can serve hundreds or even thousands of cows. But he himself derives little satisfaction from the process. He lives with a score or so of other bulls in a cattle breeding centre, occupying a cell at night and tethered with them in a pasture by day. He can see his rivals but cannot get at them for the trial of strength which his instinct tells him ought to be staged.

Life is better for bulls in countries with more spacious landscapes. In America, Australia and other lands with far horizons bulls run with their herds on extensive ranches. Even here, however, there is a tendency towards employing bulls of the more docile breeds, such as the Hereford. In Britain Herefords are frequently used with batches of heifers, and again the docility of the breed is one of the deciding factors, though others are the relatively small size of the resultant calves (making for easy calving) and the fact that the calves are colour-marked, with the Hereford's white face which clearly indicates the animal's breeding. But, armed with a light stick, I would not mind venturing into a field with a Hereford bull any day, whereas I would think twice about so tempting Providence with an Ayrshire or Friesian, and certainly not with a Jersey.

Under commercial management, bulls running free with herds are generally allowed more females than they would normally possess in the wild – from 20 to 50, or perhaps even more. We have little information on the natural ratio of bulls to cows in genuinely wild conditions, for it is long since any really wild, as distinct from feral, cattle roamed the plains and forests of the world. In herds of African buffalo, which possibly offer a parallel, adult females generally outnumber adult males by about three to one. But many of the males are non-breeding animals. There will be one dominant male – a splendid animal in his prime – which alone will mate with the females, if he can by any means prevent rivals from doing so. The younger males draw off into bachelor groups, trailing along in the rear of the main herd. In due course, one of the young males will challenge the herd bull, fight him and, if he triumphs, take his place.

The young males have an urge to excel, to challenge the authority of their elders, to achieve domination. The older males try to exercise autocratic authority and to retain it as long as possible. The females are instinctively submissive to the dominant male. Possibly because instinct tells them that he is their best protection against the dangers around them, especially during the vulnerable periods when they are

Chillingham bulls fighting; a painting by George Stubbs, 1788.

heavily pregnant or when their offspring are young, they are attracted by his masculinity.

So, then, while we may regard the tethered bulls at an A.I. centre with compassion, a wild bull, or even a captive bull showing evidence of a still rebellious spirit, can arouse in us disturbing and primitive instincts. Just what these are depends on our attitude towards naked, aggressive power. And, largely, on our sex. The feminine reaction to massive masculinity is very different from that of the male.

We look at a bull and think thoughts that are usually submerged beneath layers of convention and civilization. We see his pride, his lust, his pugnacity, his extroversion. We watch him in the context of his herd and note his rough gentleness with the females, his tolerance of the young, his determination to keep the adolescent males in

A Challenge; a wood engraving by Thomas Bewick. c.1790.

their place. We recognize in this animal behaviour our own basic instincts. Those oh so respectable and sophisticated reactions to the problems that enter our lives, are they really very different from the instinctive behaviour of cattle faced with similar predicaments?

There is a certain profound significance in the old music-hall anecdote about the two men who were relating their dreams of the previous night. Said one,

"I was lying in a lovely green field, with blue sky above me and thirty of the loveliest females in the world sprawled in seductive postures all around me. All mine."

"So you were in heaven?"

"No. A Longhorn bull on a Texas pasture."

Perhaps part of the fascination of bulls for us is that in them we sometimes catch a mirror image of ourselves.

2
The Aurochs
and Other Wild Bulls

Although most authorities distinguish two species of wild cattle from which our domestic breeds have descended, there is a growing suspicion that there may have been one only. The two types, numerous remains of which have been found in early archaeological sites, are known as *Bos primigenius* and *Bos longifrons* (also called *Bos brachyceros*). The former is the aurochs, or urus; the latter has been termed, though somewhat erroneously, the Celtic shorthorn.

Bos longifrons was a very small animal, probably not as large as a modern Jersey. It had a long, narrow face, slender bones and short, curved horns. Its remains are first found in Britain associated with Early Bronze Age sites, which indicates that it was introduced by invading tribes between 1900 and 1400 B.C. At that time a migration of peoples north-westwards from the Alpine regions of central Europe occurred, and *Bos longifrons* has been traced to those areas. It did not necessarily originate there but could well have been brought by peoples from central Asia or the Near East.

At one time it was thought that the earliest cattle found in Britain belonged to this type, but now it has been established that *Bos primigenius* was there at least 500 years before. Whether or not it was domesticated is not known, for its remains have been found in circumstances which suggest that the carcases had been used for meat.

The suggestion that both types were originally one – the aurochs – is based on a reconstruction of what may have happened during the long millenia through which the process of domestication went on. We can imagine that the earliest domesticated cattle were those reared from calves found in thickets where their mothers had hidden them, or captured after their mothers had been killed. As herds were thus built up, they began to perpetuate themselves by breeding. But the animals which lent themselves best to domestication would obviously be the most docile ones.

Not many years ago I encountered in southern India an example of the sort of thing that could well have gone on. I visited a farm of which the manager, though well versed in the arts of crop husbandry, had little knowledge of livestock. Rather reluctantly, he showed me his pigs – a herd of between 20 and 30 scraggy, bristly, diminutive, razor-backed animals. Pigs of all ages were running together. A runt of a sow was pointed out to me as one which had recently farrowed. She had produced only two piglets, one of which had promptly died.

Pigs were not really valued as commercial livestock in that part of India. They were for feasts, on special occasions. About a fortnight before my visit such a feast had occurred, and the villagers had asked the farm manager for a pig for the table. Naturally he had been pleased to oblige, and naturally he had killed the biggest animal he had. The only boar of service age! If it had ever occurred to him that he would have to wait a long time before any more piglets would be born, he would doubtless dismiss that as a minor consideration. He could wait until a young boar had grown mature enough to become a sire. Time was not important.

A similar attitude towards stock-breeding could well have prevailed among many of our remote ancestors. If so, it could explain how the massive, fierce, big-boned aurochs (*Bos primigenius*) deteriorated into the small, fragile shorthorn (*Bos longi-frons*).

The aurochs was a forest, marshland and grassland species. It roamed over Europe and Asia, even north Africa, moving northwards as the forest took over from prairie in the wake of the receding ice after the last Ice Age. It is depicted in numerous cave paintings, some of which may date to between 20,000 and 30,000 years ago. Some of these paintings, as at Lascaux, Altamira and other sites in northern Spain and south-western France, are extraordinarily lifelike and display remarkable artistic ability. Lascaux has the portrait of a bull with long, upcurved horns, apparently standing at bay. It is red in colour, with darker (blackish-brown) head and neck, and a white stripe (finching) along the backbone (see opposite page 17).

Paintings of the eighth millennium B.C. show that the Maglemosian men of that period were hunting aurochs with bows and arrows. Others in central Anatolia of 6000 to 5700 B.C. indicate the baiting of wild bulls. At the Kom Ombo sites in Upper Egypt aurochs' bones are found in association with palaeolithic settlements. On the Tassili plateau in the central Sahara rock-paintings dated at about 3000 B.C., when the Sahara was evidently a grassy plain, depict a hunt in which men with bows and arrows are surrounding and shooting at large bulls and cows with very long, sickle-shaped horns. Some of the animals are coloured reddish-brown, others are pied – brown and white (see opposite page 16).

Most writers refer to the aurochs as a gigantic animal. Evidently it stood 6 feet or so high at the shoulders and was massive in proportion. Julius Caesar comments that

14

Bushmen driving off stolen cattle; from rock paintings in a cave near Hermon, South Africa.

some aurochs were almost as big as elephants. An old English poem, perhaps the oldest in existence, the Rune Song, thus describes the aurochs:

> The aurochs is proud and extravagantly horned;
> A very fierce beast, it fights with its horns,
> Marching mightily across the moors,
> It is a most courageous creature.

Anthony Dent, who has dug deep into the subject, says in his *Lost Beasts of Britain* (1974) that "the more spectacular form more or less resembled a Red Devon bull 18 hands high (6 feet), dark red in colour with a white streak down the spine". On the other hand, the resurrected aurochs bred by Heinz Heck, of which I have seen a fine example in Budapest Zoo, more nearly resembles in colour a Jersey bull, showing various shades of colour from fulvous yellow to black.

Anthony Dent examines the problem of whether the aurochs survived in Britain

15

into historic times but decides against it. The English poem quoted above, he says, was composed on the Continent before the Angles and Saxons came to Britain. Various references to *bubali* in medieval documents down to the thirteenth century are, he considers, to feral animals. During the troubled centuries when Britain was undergoing invasion by Anglo-Saxons and Vikings there must have been many occasions when cattle, their owners slain or fugitives, escaped to the forests and resumed a wild way of life. In 1174 an English writer, William FitzStephen, refers to the existence, very near London, of "an immense forest, woody ranges, hiding-places of wild beasts, of stags, of fallow deer, of boars, and of forest bulls". And as late as 1603 George Owen, in *Description of Pembrokeshire*, mentions "I have also seen good pastime in the hunting and killing of the wild bull". Owen adds, however, that these wild bulls had owners, so perhaps we may assume that they were the seventeenth-century counterpart of the cattle that today wander in the New Forest, apparently free but very much private property. They would, however, evidently have been much fiercer and wilder, more like the Chillingham cattle.

There is, of course, the likelihood that after a few generations domesticated cattle which escaped to the wild reverted to the original type. The medieval "wild bulls" of English forests may therefore quite well have resembled the aurochs which had been their remote ancestor.

It was this tendency to revert to type which was exploited by Dr. Heinz Heck, director of the Tierpark Hellabrunn, Munich, in his imaginative and successful programme to resurrect the aurochs. Soon after the First World War he began to wonder whether the genetical process by which a dairy cow, capable of producing 2,000 gallons of milk a year and which was evolved from the most unpromising material over many generations, could not be made to work in reverse. He started his experiments in 1921. Taking examples of breeds and cross-breeds of cattle from many parts of Europe, from Hungary to the Scottish Highlands and from the Netherlands to Corsica, he selected from each generation the individuals which best represented some outstanding feature of the aurochs. The size, the long legs, the colouring, the great horns, the white finching, all were duly established. By 1932 he had two animals, one of each sex, which corresponded to the descriptions and paintings of the aurochs which had become extinct more than 300 years ago.

Soon after Dr. Heck began his experiments at Munich his brother, Professor Lutz

(Right) Prehistoric rock paintings of about 3000 B.C. from Jabbaren, on the Tassili plateau, in the Sahara, depicting hunters and wild cattle.

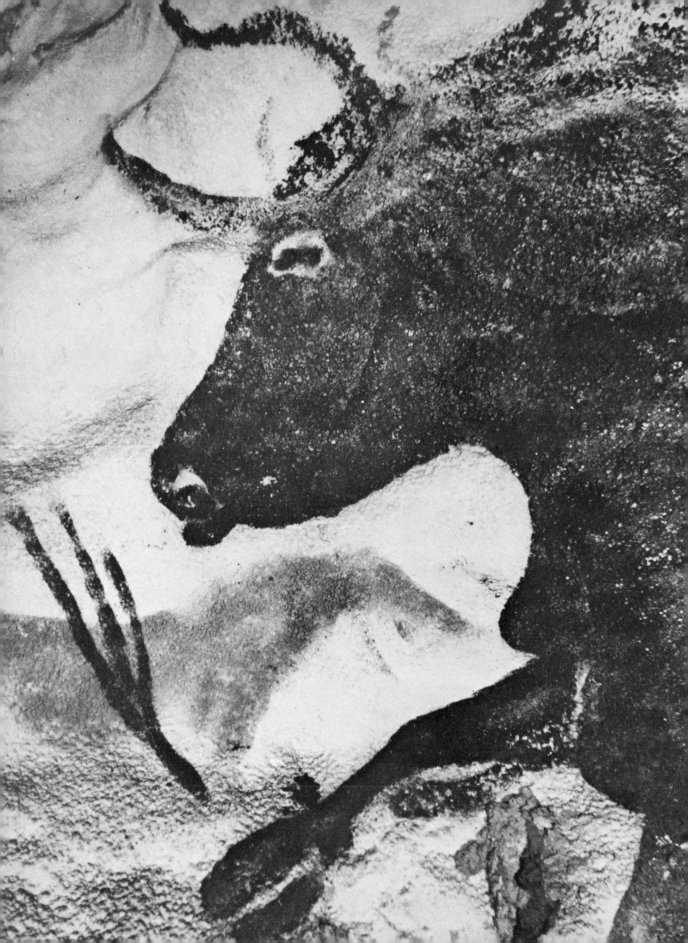

Heck, started a similar programme at Berlin Zoo. Working with an entirely different basic collection of stock, mostly from the herds of Spanish and French fighting bulls, he too produced living aurochsen. Remarkably, the Berlin aurochsen were, despite their different ancestry, indistinguishable from the Munich specimens.

As the programmes continued it might have been anticipated that, from such a hotch-potch of basic stock, a bizarre collection of freaks and throw-backs might appear. Not a bit of it. Once the type had been established, the further generations of calves were completely true to it. Some were a little darker than others, as happened among the original aurochsen, but not a single throw-back occurred.

Two other remarkable features of the new race of aurochs were observed. Although bred largely from domestic cattle, they quickly reverted to the characteristics of the wild. They evidently had a very keen sense of smell and became suspicious, vicious and decidedly dangerous. Some of the Berlin herd, released around Bialowieza, in Poland, during the last war, settled down immediately to a wild life.

The other, and perhaps even more surprising, feature displayed by these new aurochsen was their ability to resist disease. They could not escape the epidemics of foot-and-mouth disease which swept the herds of Germany in the years before the Second World War, but whereas domestic cattle were very seriously affected and had to be slaughtered by the thousand, the aurochsen showed only very slight symptoms for a few days and had soon completely recovered. Much the same happened with rheumatic fever, another cattle plague of which Germany suffered from severe epidemics.

Dr. Heinz Heck and his brother were moved by pure scientific curiosity to conduct their experiments. Inspired by the old pictures and descriptions of the aurochs, they wanted to see whether, by genetic manipulation, it was possible to reconstruct it. The task proved even easier than they had expected, far easier than to breed a first-class milk-producing cow from nondescript stock.

What, however, they achieved for the sake of science may prove of the greatest value to commercial cattle-breeders, whose stock provide millions of humans with milk and meat. We strive to produce better beef, more milk, higher butterfat percentages and more handsome cows, using artificial insemination, implanted foetuses, in-breeding and other modern technical aids. It is at least conceivable that our demands for higher productivity may be subjecting our domestic cattle to such

(Left) *Head of great black bull, from the cave paintings at Lascaux, Dordogne, France. 15,000–20,000* B.C.

severe stresses that they are losing their resistance to disease. At some future date we may be glad to go back to the sound, original stock as represented by the new aurochsen for genes that will restore the lost stamina of our domestic herds.

*   *   *

If the small, short-horned *Bos longifrons* was really a derivation from *Bos primigenius*, the aurochs, as the majority of modern authorities now conclude, what of other types of wild cattle? Have any of the species that still exist made contributions to our domestic stock? And were there other extinct breeds that should be noticed?

The last question is difficult to answer. Reference has been made to the hunting scene depicted in the rock paintings of Jabbaren, in the Sahara. Naked men with bows and arrows are killing long-horned cattle of aurochs type. But when that painting was made cattle had already been domesticated in both Egypt and Mesopotamia for at least a thousand years. Oxen were pulling ploughs and carts, cows were being milked, butter and cheese was being made, and cattle were being fed on crops harvested and stored especially for them.

On page 121 is a reference to a dwarf type of bull, illustrated on a tomb painting of the time of the Pharaoh Amenemhet (around 2000 B.C.). Although tiny, standing no more than about 30 inches high, it has the long, lyre-shaped horns typical of most Egyptian cattle. But the Egyptians also had a polled breed. On murals we can see them shown side by side with horned cattle. Were these a breed developed by Egyptian stockmen by selective breeding, or was a polled wild species involved? We do not know. But certainly there was time in those long millenia for many experiments and many developments.

One of the features of the ancient aurochs was its straight back. Contemporary writers testify that it was not humped, and numerous pictures confirm this. But many modern breeds possess very heavy shoulders, almost amounting to a hump, as do even some of the Spanish fighting bulls, which are often supposed to be directly descended from the aurochs.

This hump is almost certainly derived from the Indian zebu, which can be considered another of the ancestors of our domestic cattle. The zebu is in general a big animal, taller than most European breeds (though there are some small varieties), and it has this fatty hump over the withers or shoulders. It is rather long in the leg, has a pronounced dewlap and possesses long, up-curved and generally powerful horns. Its home is India, where it is abundant, but it is also found in China and in much of Africa.

18

It seems that trade existed between Mesopotamia and Egypt at a very early period and that one of the articles of commerce was cattle, for zebu-type animals certainly found their way into Egypt in dynastic times. That, however, is not surprising, for the history of civilization is one of intermittent setbacks through the irruption of barbarous nomadic tribes. In almost every instance these invaders have been livestock men, counting their wealth in flocks and herds. They came from the great plains of central Asia and European Russia, from which there are ancient routes into the settled lands of India, Mesopotamia and Egypt. So the mechanics for a frequent interchange of livestock between all those countries were present. It is not surprising that we find traces of zebu influence in places distant from the home of the breed, as in the Maremma cattle of southern Italy.

We have noted that aurochs roamed the Sahara in those distant centuries when it was a grassy prairie. As the land dried up and became a desert, the great cattle must have retreated into congenial territory around the margins. We know that they were found in the swamps by the river Nile and on the plains of the coastal regions of North Africa. Presumably, too, they penetrated into the savannah zone south of the desert. Whether they extended their range right through the tropics to the South African veldt is not known, but it seems quite likely, for the early Dutch settlers found the resident Hottentots keeping a large, long-horned red breed of cattle which have become known as Afrikander.

But the zebu, too, has made an important contribution to the cattle of Africa. Apart from early infiltration, it was introduced to Egypt in considerable numbers by the Arab invaders in the seventh century A.D. From Egypt the conquering Arabs and their cattle moved southwards into the Sudan and thence into most of East Africa. In the Appendix we take a closer look at some of the present-day African cattle types and breeds, but in general it is possible to trace zebu influence throughout East Africa at least as far south as Zululand. The abundant Boran and Jiddu cattle of Kenya and Ethiopia are of obvious zebu origin, with massive humps and prominent pendulous dewlaps. On the other hand throughout much of West Africa and linking up with zebu territory south of the Sahara is a straight-backed type with long, wide-spanned horns, which would seem to have descended directly from the aurochs without zebu admixture. There are also pockets of cattle of this type in countries where zebus are predominant, as in the Nuba mountains of Kordofan, in the Sudan. And it is interesting that many of these animals are parti-coloured, like those depicted in the Jabbaren paintings. However, there may be an element of human selection at work here, for spotted cattle have long been valued by many African peoples, the colour pattern being attractive on the shields made from their hides.

Although the zebu influence is traceable in Zulu cattle, the hump is not nearly as pronounced as in types farther north. Nor is it in the Afrikander cattle, though it is definitely present. Incidentally, a characteristic of the zebu is that it does not low or bellow, like cattle of aurochs descent, but grunts. The Afrikander cattle have the European not the zebu voice-sound.

The three main types of cattle, the aurochs (*Bos primigenius*), the Celtic shorthorn (*Bos longifrons*) and the zebu (*Bos indicus*) are by most authorities regarded as subspecies of *Bos taurus*; and, as we have noted, some consider *Bos longifrons* to be derived from *Bos primigenius*. *Bos taurus* is the only species in the genus *Bos*. Hence these may be regarded as the only true cattle. However, the family Bovinae has a number of other genera, most of which have several species.

GAUR (Bibos gaurus) (sometimes included in the genus *Bos* and known as *Bos gaurus*)

The gaur is a huge animal, whose home is in the forests of India, Burma and Malaya. It is sometimes known as the Indian bison, though it is not a true bison. Anyone who has seen a gaur can appreciate the ancient references to the aurochs as a beast standing 6 feet high at the shoulders. That is the stature of a mature gaur bull, which may weigh over a ton. It has fairly long, stout horns curved upwards from its skull like crescent moons. It has a pronounced dorsal ridge and a large hump on the shoulders, which give it a humped, buffalo-like appearance.

Although it has a reputation for ferocity, that probably depends on its willingness and ability to defend itself when cornered or wounded. It has in the past been much pestered by hunters, seeking the magnificent heads of the bulls for trophies. Some of the preserved horns measure 40 inches across, which is probably ten inches more than any likely to be encountered today. Now, although hunting and persecution continue, the chief danger to its continued existence is the destruction of its habitat, by agricultural, forestry and other ill-co-ordinated schemes. In India it survives mainly in wild-life reserves, primarily in the western Ghats and in the foothills of the Himalayas, but it has become rare. Even in what are supposed to be sanctuaries it is in constant danger from poachers, who can get good money for the meat, skin and horns.

The gaur is sufficiently nearly related to domestic cattle to interbreed with them, and from time to time a gaur bull will mate with cows from a wandering herd. There is a name for such hybrids, *mithun*; they have straight horns instead of curved. Unfortunately contact with domestic cattle does the gaur no good, for it is susceptible to many of the diseases which afflict India's herds. Epidemics are known to have caused heavy mortality from time to time.

20

Gaur do not thrive in captivity, and very few zoos have specimens. It is said that three or four hundred years ago the people of Assam used to keep domestic gaur, but the secret of taming them has evidently been lost.

In Malaya the gaur is known as the *Seladang*.

GAYAL *(Bibos, or Bos, frontalis)*

There is evidently some confusion about this animal. Most authorities classify it as a separate species, with specific name as above. But Balakrishna Seshadri, the Indian author, puts it down (in his *The Twilight of Indian Wild Life*) as a hybrid between the gaur and domestic cattle – identical, in short, with the *mithun*. He says, "These hybrids apparently live in a semi-wild state in the vicinity of villages, but I do not known if they are put to any use." Fifty years earlier George Jennison, curator of Belle Vue Zoo, Manchester, wrote that it "exists in large numbers in a semi-domesticated state" but adds that there are also wild gayal, which are "rare and very shy". He records the interesting note that "a hybrid between it and the zebu has bred with an American bison", which is an indication of the near relationship between these species of the family Bovinae.

In general the gayal tends to be smaller than the gaur, perhaps because of the influence of domestic cattle, but it has the same massive, humped body. Its horns are straight or only slightly curved.

INDIAN BUFFALO *(Bos, or Bubalis, bubalis)*

The Indian or water buffalo is one of the common domestic animals of India, where I have often heard it referred to as the "brake-tester", due to its habit of resting in the middle of busy roads, often just around a tricky corner. The epithet draws attention to the reluctance of any motorist to collide with one of these formidable road hazards; the car will almost inevitably suffer more than the buffalo. Although domesticated, the buffalo has a mind of its own. It will co-operate but it will not be forced. If upset, it reverts quickly to savagery, and a buffalo weighing up to a ton is not an animal to be trifled with. Yet in its normal docile mood it can be led or ridden by a child.

Enormously powerful, the buffalo has huge horns sometimes measuring ten or twelve feet around the curve. The wild buffalo is quite capable of holding its own against the tiger, which, however, hesitates to attack any but young calves. But the wild buffalo has become scarce. Balakrishna Seshadri considers that it is now extinct in north Bengal, where it was once abundant, and that it survives only in small numbers in reserves in Assam, Orissa, Madhya Pradesh and perhaps Nepal. Assam has the largest population, estimated at 1,425 individuals, mostly in two reserves.

The vitual extermination of the buffalo in much of north-eastern India and Bangladesh has been due entirely to human persecution, for this formidable animal has few enemies other than man. The Indian peasants have, however, some reason for their intermittent warfare with wild buffalo, which invade their cultivated fields by night and create havoc amid the crops.

Wild buffalo inhabit country where the chief vegetation is tall, dense jungle-grass, high enough to hide them completely. On hot days they love to wallow in mud and water, often submerging until only their noses project above the surface. The resultant coat of mud helps to protect them against insect bites.

BANTENG *(Bibos, or Bos, banteng)*

The banteng is a rather smaller and slenderer edition of the gaur, found in south-eastern Asia, from Burma to Malaysia. It has lighter horns and prefers open forest country, with frequent glades, to dense woods and jungles. Little is known of its present status, though it is likely to have been affected by war and other recent human activities.

ANOA *(Anoa depressicornis)*

This is a dwarf type of cattle or buffalo, sometimes known as the ox antelope. It is found on wooded mountain slopes on the island of Celebes, in Indonesia. One of the smallest of all wild cattle, it stands only just over three feet at the shoulder. There is a suggestion that its diminutive size is due to long inbreeding in its restricted island habitat (though it must be added that that does not always produce dwarf types of animal). It is blackish in colour and has short, almost upright, straight horns.

TAMARAU *(Anoa mindorensis)*

Found only on the Philippine island of Mindoro, the tamarau is very similar to the anoa, though slightly larger.

CAPE BUFFALO *(Syncerus caffer caffer)*

Africa also has a wild buffalo, the Cape buffalo, so-called because it was in Cape Colony that it first became familiar to Europeans, though it is now extinct in the wild in South Africa. Elsewhere in Africa it is found from Mozambique to the fringe of the

Sahara. Jennison, writing in 1927, said that rinderpest had decimated the herds in many areas, but the species now seems to have recovered, except in regions from which it has been squeezed out by agricultural and industrial development, and in East Africa it is widely distributed and common. A huge, blackish-brown animal, standing five feet or more at the shoulder, it has thick, strongly curved horns and is a most formidable fighter. Even lions, except young and inexperienced ones, will give an adult bull a wide berth, though they will snap up unwary or straggling calves. Matched against man, it is a cunning adversary, capable of springing an ambush or of feigning a retreat when its enemy has taken refuge in a tree.

Its habits are similar to those of the wild Indian buffalo. It likes reedy swamp country, where it can submerge for much of the day, acquiring a coating of mud to protect it against ticks and insects. It forages and drinks at twilight, both morning and evening. The herds tend to be larger than those of the Indian buffalo, number-

Cape Buffalo bull.

ing sometimes as many as a hundred animals, and during the dry season several herds may congregate at one water-hole. But, again as with Indian buffalo, the adult males, some of which weigh nearly 2,000 lb, often prefer to draw off by themselves or with a few male companions, returning to the herds only for the mating season.

CONGO BUFFALO *(Syncerus caffer nanus)*

Also known as the Bush Cow, the Congo buffalo inhabits the dense rain forests of Zaire. It is considerably smaller than the Cape buffalo, standing about $3\frac{1}{2}$ feet at the shoulder and weighing some 450 lb. It retains its reddish-brown calf colour all its life. Its scientific name denotes that it is regarded as only a subspecies of the Cape buffalo.

EUROPEAN BISON *(Bison bonasus)*

The European bison is a species which has survived by the narrowest possible margin. A contemporary of the aurochs, it had vanished from much of central Europe by the eleventh century and by the end of the nineteenth century was to be found in only a few protected forests in Lithuania and the Caucasus. In the two wars, and due to activity between them, the wild herds were wiped out, but some survived in captivity in Lithuania. Some of these were subsequently released in the Bialowieza Forest, on the Polish-Russian border, and have multiplied, quickly relapsing into wild behaviour.

The European bison has longer legs than the more familiar American bison and a full-grown bull can stand over 6 feet high at the shoulder. It has a moderate hump, though not so pronounced as that of the American bison, and the shoulder hair is less dense and shaggy. Its horns are lighter and more curved. It is a forest animal rather than a grazer of grassy plains and is shy, being adept at concealing itself among trees.

AMERICAN BISON *(Bison bison)*

Few large animals are more familiar, through films and photographs, than the American bison, though most people have now seen living animals only in zoological collections. The species was saved from extinction in the nick of time but is now flourishing again on reserves in the United States and Canada.

When America was discovered by Europeans the bison must have been one of the most abundant of large animals on the face of the earth. Its home was the great grass prairie of central North America, an area nearly 4,000 miles long from north to

Herd of American Bison being stalked by Indians wearing white wolf-skins. An engraving after a painting by George Catlin made in the 1830's.

south, and 2,000 miles broad. On these plains it was migratory, moving north in spring and south in autumn, creating, as it did so, the wide tracks worn by generations of hooves and known to settlers of the West as "buffalo trails". The numbers were past counting. An eye-witness says that "they covered the earth seemingly as one vast brown buffalo robe".

Tribes of Indians followed them along the migration routes, taking a heavy toll by such wasteful hunting methods as stampeding hundreds of them over cliffs, but it made little difference to the overall total. The doom of the species was sealed when the Canadian Pacific Railway drove its iron rails right across the continent, opening up the prairies to settlement. Agriculture and migratory herds of bison were incompatible, and the animals were slaughtered by tens of thousands. Even as late as 1871, when the massacre had begun, a traveller "drove for 25 miles along the Arkansas River through an unbroken herd of buffaloes. It was the great southern herd on its annual migration northward, and at that date it is estimated by naturalists that this herd totalled about 3,500,000 animals. At that period, too, the northern herd contained about 1,500,000. In those days mighty herds of buffaloes frequently stopped or derailed railway trains and obstructed the progress of boats on the Mississippi River."

By 1908 a census revealed only 2,047 bison left in the world, of which 1,722 were in captivity. Energetic efforts were then made to create reserves for them. By 1914 the population had increased to 3,800; by 1927 to 8,000; and today it probably exceeds 50,000. The bison is safe from extinction, but never again will the magnificent sight of millions of bison on trek across the prairies be seen.

The American bison is a humped animal, with very heavy forequarters and a massive, shaggy head. An adult bull can stand 6 feet high at the shoulder and weigh more than a ton. Cows are considerably lighter. Most of the body is covered with soft, woolly hair which, on the hindquarters and belly, is moulted in spring. On the forequarters the hair is much longer and shaggier, forming a thick, curly mane, with beard, crest, leg feathers and neck mantle to match.

The bison is a grazer and, indeed, it kept the American prairies treeless by eating off any seedling trees that appeared. Its herd instinct is naturally strong, each herd having its dominant male, of whom subordinate males keep well clear. But it seems that on the great migrations the leader was generally an old and experienced cow.

YAK (*Poephagus,* or *Bos, grunniens*)

The yak is best known as a domestic animal of Tibet, to the inhabitants of which bleak, windswept land it supplies milk and meat as well as acting as a beast of burden. It is, however, still found wild in parts of Tibet and in some of the remoter provinces of western China. It is admirably adapted to life in an austere, inhospitable climate, characterized by sub-zero temperatures for much of the year. Its body is densely clothed with thick hair, which hangs down like a ragged overcoat on flanks, belly and legs. Its hooves are large and rounded, to give a grip on snow and ice, and it can live comfortably on a diet of mosses and lichen, eating snow to obtain water.

There is a general impression that the yak is not a large animal – an erroneous impression created by those seen solely in zoological collections. In its native country a mature bull yak may stand as high as 6 feet at the shoulders. It is a truly massive animal, with great, powerful, humped shoulders, like an American bison, and a formidable pair of horns, which extend horizontally and then curve upwards. As each horn can be 3 feet long and the forehead is broad, their total span is impressive. The wild yak bull is said to be a ferocious and dangerous animal, but the domesticated yaks are usually quite docile.

26

Bull Yak.

The yak will interbreed with domestic cattle, and the crossbreds are said to make the best working animals.

MUSK-OX *(Ovibos moschatus)*

The musk-ox has its home in an even colder region than the hardy yak, for it inhabits the northern fringe of Arctic Canada and the northern parts of Greenland, where it remains active in winter temperatures of $-90°$F. To adapt itself for survival in such a climate it grows a double coat, consisting of an under-layer of dense, soft wool protected by an overcoat of long, coarse hair which reaches almost to the ground. It even has hair between the hooves. In winter it moves to windswept areas where the snow lies sufficiently shallow to permit the animals to scrape it aside with their hooves, revealing frozen grasses, sedges and other plants beneath.

The musk-ox has a bison-like hump and indeed resembles a small bison. An adult bull will stand about $4\frac{1}{2}$ feet at the shoulder and weigh 800–900 lb. It has a wide frontal plate from which the horns curve first downwards, then outwards and upwards. The frontal plate itself is sometimes 6 to 9 inches thick, giving ample protection when two bulls charge each other. In their behaviour at mating time, when the contending bulls will draw off and then cannon into each other with a resounding crash, musk-oxen resemble sheep rather than cattle, and some zoologists think that they are the more nearly related to sheep.

Musk-oxen naturally do not greatly enjoy life in a warmer climate than their own and so are not often seen in zoos. But it is said that some found their way into Roman arenas during the period of the games, and that the Romans knew how to differentiate between them and the more familiar aurochs and bison.

TAKIN (Budoras taxicolor)

The takin is another link between cattle and sheep and probably the nearest existing relation of the musk-ox, though some authorities note its similarity to other families of the animal kingdom by terming it a "goat-antelope". A heavily-built animal with a bovine head and short, strongly-curved horns, it stands about 4 feet at the shoulders. Its hair is short but thick, but it does have a small beard.

Living in inaccessible country in the mountainous region between India and China and along the south-eastern foothills of the Himalayas, the takin is said to conceal itself in rhododendron thickets and so is seldom seen. It is agile and surefooted on precipitous cliffs. Not much is known of its habits.

WILD WHITE CATTLE

As recounted on page 16, in times of prolonged war and social disorders domestic cattle have wandered away and become feral. The best-known examples are the British wild white cattle, which still maintain their independent existence, particularly at Chillingham, in Northumberland.

Their recorded history starts in 1220, when a stone wall was erected around Chillingham Park, separating it from the great Caledonian Forest and isolating a herd of wild cattle within the enclosure. During that period it has experienced considerable fluctuations in numbers, being at one time down to 13 animals, but at present it totals, I think, nearly 50. The ratio of males to females is fairly constant at about two or three. The Chillingham herd has as its disposal 365 acres, of which about 100 acres are woodland and the rest rough grazing, with much bracken. It usually spends the day in the wood and comes out to feed in the evening.

A Chillingham bull will stand 5 to 6 feet high at the shoulders and is strong and sturdily built. The coat colour is creamy-white, with muzzle, hooves and tips of horns black, and the ears dark brown, black or red. Jennison says "they can run like horses, climb like goats and have been known to clear a 6-foot fence by a stand-jump". But most visitors – and large numbers come to the park each summer – generally see only a contented group of white cattle chewing the cud, though whether the animals would be quite as docile as they appear if the safety fence were removed is another matter. There is a Chillingham Wild White Cattle Association which ensures the survival and well-being of the herd and of which the Earl of Tankerville, who owns the park, is President. Other herds of wild white cattle are found on a number of estates in northern England, Wales and Scotland. The animals are all similar to the Chillingham cattle, though with some minor variations.

The herd organization and social behaviour of the Chillingham cattle is discussed in the final chapter; here we briefly examine theories about their origin. As other herds are found in widely scattered localities where they have been given protection, we may assume that wild white cattle were once found in suitable country throughout northern Britain, including Scotland and North Wales.

Leaving aside early references to wild cattle of which the colour was not specified, such as the wild bulls which William FitzStephen saw in Epping Forest towards the end of the twelfth century, we find a number of records of white animals. The laws of the Welsh prince, Howell Dda, in the tenth century, mention white cattle with red ears. The Scottish writer, Hector Boece (in *Scotorum Historiae*, 1526) refers to white bulls "with crisp and curling manes, like fierce lions . . . that were more wild than any other beasts". In 1576 four men were charged with killing "white kye and bulls" in Cumbernauld Forest, in Dumbartonshire. A herd of wild white cattle lived in the grounds of Drumlanrig Castle, Dumfriesshire, until 1780 and were noted for their ferocity. The naturalist Pennant, who saw them, says they had black muzzles and black rims to their eyes; also that they were medium-sized animals with very long legs. Another eye-witness noted that the inside of the ear was red and that the horns were black-tipped. "Some of the bulls have a thin upright mane about $1\frac{1}{2}$ or 2 inches long." Several other herds were destroyed or dispersed in the middle years of the eighteenth century, because they were so untameable and dangerous in a countryside that was becoming increasingly civilized. The herd at Chartley Park, Staffordshire (see opposite page 112), was enclosed when the park was fenced in 1248 for the Earl of Ferrers. Here again white was the predominant colour, and the birth

29

of a black or piebald calf was held to betoken a death in the Earl's family. On page 103 it is noted that the British White cattle, a domesticated dual-purpose breed evidently derived from the same ancestry as the wild white herds, has similar colour markings, though the breed is polled, not horned. In folklore many instances occur of fairy cattle being white with red ears (as also of pigs!).

Where, then, did these clearly-marked white cattle originate? One theory, supported by a number of authorities, is that they have descended from cattle brought to Britain by the Romans. They could have belonged to the ancient Maremma breed or one similar, though the colour of the modern Maremma is not identical with that of the British wild whites. Another theory is that they are descended from the aurochs, perhaps through a type of *Bos longifrons*.

An objection to that theory is that, although the aurochs showed considerable variability in colour, it seldom if ever appears to have been white. To this the protagonists of the idea reply that the very rarity of the colour might account for its survival and establishment as a stable feature. We are asked to imagine ourselves back in the dawn of time. The domestication of livestock is beginning but the practice of breeding from them is not fully established. We are walking through a forest when we spot in a mass of bracken a calf left there by its mother. What colour is most conspicuous and therefore most likely to be seen? White. There is also the possibility that a white calf would be rejected by the herd, as something different and therefore not to be tolerated. Thus a tribe would acquire a basic breeding stock of white cattle – white because white is such an unusual colour among wild animals of the species.

While all this may be true, it could apply to the domestication of cattle anywhere. It is not incompatible with the theory that the wild white British cattle did not originate in Britain but were introduced in Roman times. The Druids, however, preceded Julius Caesar in the story of Britain, and the Druids are known to have sacrificed bulls. Pliny, writing in A.D. 77, says that the Druids,

> having made preparation for sacrifice and a banquet beneath the trees, they bring thither two white bulls, whose horns are bound then for the first time . . . They then kill the victims, praying that God will render this gift of his propitious to those to whom he has granted it.

Pliny's information came mostly from Gaul, but the practices of the British Druids seem to have been very similar. As also were those of the Druids of Ireland, whither the Romans never penetrated.

30

The belief that a white bull was the most acceptable to the gods was very widespread in the ancient world. It was one of the tenets of Mithraism as well as, apparently, of Druidism. It is therefore at least feasible that herds of white cattle, dedicated to the gods and tended by priests, were kept in many countries. The British wild white cattle may be descendants of these.

WILD CATTLE IN AMERICA

Apart from the fighting bulls sent over to appear in the bull rings of Mexico and other cities following the Spanish Conquest, large numbers of ordinary cattle were also exported to the New World. They were mostly of a long-horned type thought by some authorities to have come from North Africa. Great herds soon became established in the New World, living on such extensive ranges of semi-arid pastures that many became more or less feral.

From these sprang the Texas Longhorns, which, when the American prairies were opened up for cattle-raising after the Civil War, were really the only animals on hand in any numbers to take advantage of the situation. By then they had had more than 300 years to adapt themselves to the sub-tropics of America and had evolved into an extremely hardy type. They were, however, very variable in appearance. Some of the cows had medium-sized, up-curved horns not unlike those of the Ayrshire; others had enormous, handle-bar horns, with a span as great as the length of the body. The bulls' horns were mostly horizontal and straight, except for an upward tilt at the ends. They resembled in many respects the English Longhorns but displayed a wider range of colours, with much red and brindle but also with many piebald and skewbald individuals. Some specimens show more white than any other colour. Pictures of the Texas Longhorn show a distinct affinity with those depicted in the rock paintings of the Sahara and on the murals of Knossos.

3

Bull Gods

Just as children personify their toys and other familiar inanimate objects, so primitive men assigned human and superhuman attributes to natural features of their environment. In a world the mechanics of which were largely unknown, they regarded with superstitious reverence springs and fast-flowing rivers, ancient trees and great stones. Everything had a spirit, which had power to affect human lives for good or ill.

Because there was nothing else with which to compare them, these spirits were likened to humans. Men made gods in their own image. In addition to gods who were rooted to specific places, there were weather gods, who controlled the rain, the frost, the winds and the burning sun. And there were wandering spirits, whom one could often hear but never see – manifestations which we would now identify as owls, nightjars, lovesick vixens and suchlike nocturnal creatures. Animals such as bears and wolves were obvious candidates for the heavenly pantheon, as, of course, were bulls.

The bull was one of the most popular gods of antiquity. His stature, strength and savagery made an even more powerful appeal to our remote ancestors than they do to us. To tribes dwelling on the fringe of the primeval forest, the great bulls which lurked in its glades must have represented a fearsome menace. Imagine gathering wild raspberries in a ferny clearing and suddenly coming face to face with one of these snorting, pawing monsters, clearly preparing for the kill. It would be enough to give a man, let alone a child, nightmares for weeks – if he survived the encounter. And often, too, these great forest demons could be heard roaring, making the woods for miles around echo to the challenges they bellowed to each other. No wonder that

(Right) *Winged man-headed bull from a doorway in the palace of Assur-nasir-pal, king of Assyria, 885–860* B.C.

in so many religions the bull god was also the god of thunder. And bull-roarers, which are simple devices that, when twirled rapidly around the head, produce a sound similar to the bellowing of a bull, were among the earliest inventions of Stone Age men.

One of the early empires of the Middle East which identified its weather-god with the bull was that of the Hittites, which flourished from about 1700 to 1220 B.C. Its capital was Hattusas, later known as Boghazköy, in Asia Minor. In the numerous bas-reliefs and other art forms which have survived the wreck of this empire, the weather-god is sometimes represented as a bull and in others as a man in a chariot drawn by two sacred bulls, whose names are Seri and Hurri. When the weather-god stands in his chariot he is sometimes depicted as wielding a thunderbolt. In one epic, of which only fragments survive, the son of the weather-god, preparing for battle, called for the sacred bulls and at the same time summoned a thunderstorm to his aid.

In contrast to the Semitic nations who were predominant over much of the Middle East at that period, the Hittites belonged to the Indo-European group of peoples. As such they were related not only to the Teutons and Celts but to the Aryan Indians, and it is therefore not surprising to find similarities between their beliefs and those of the Hindus. That the bull and cow were sacred to the early Aryans is understandable. They entered India, by way of the mountain passes, from the grassy steppes of central Asia where they had lived a nomadic life, following their herds on seasonal migrations. Professor Stuart Piggott, writing in *Prehistoric India*, notes that the Aryan language has separate words for "a cow with a strange calf", "a cow barren after calving", "a three-year-old ox" and other animals in the all-important herds.

> Red, black, dappled and light-coloured cows are mentioned, and herds were differentiated by distinctive nicks cut in the ears . . . The cows were milked three times a day, and castration was practised, oxen being used for the normal purposes of farm transport, and beef was freely eaten as the main meat dish. "Slaying cows for guests" was an attribute of highest praise to an Aryan squire, and Indra was a champion beef-eater.

In Aryan religion Nandi, the sacred bull, was the leader of Siva's attendants.

When a wealthy person died his relations had to select the finest bull calf available

(Left) *Bull's head in gold and lapis lazuli from a lyre found in the royal burial ground at Ur, Sumeria, 3500–2750 B.C.*

Terracotta bull, dating from about 2500 B.C., in the National Museum, New Delhi. Note zebu type with pendulous dewlap.

and dedicate it to Nandi. At the funeral ceremony the Brahman priest branded the bull and turned it loose, to wander wherever it chose. No one was allowed to work or destroy or in any way interfere with such a bull, which could help itself to cultivated crops with impunity.

There is a legend to the effect that a certain king of long ago established this custom by decree in order to improve the standard of the livestock in his dominions. He reasoned that if these Brahmini bulls, all of the highest standard, were allowed to roam freely they would mate with the village cows and so gradually up-grade the stock. At first his programme was safeguarded by the appointment of local committees, of farmers and cattle-breeders, whose duty it was to assess the value of bulls offered to the priests and to make sure that they came up to standard. Later the procedure became slipshod, and any cheap bull-calf was accepted. Thus a practise initiated with the best of intentions degenerated into one which had the opposite effect to what was desired.

The present sanctity accorded to cattle in India is a natural development of the tremendous value attached to them by the early Aryan ancestors of the Hindus. "Never forget the debt you owe to cattle," declared Indra. "To you they are sacred."

And so they are to the pious Hindu to this day, although it seems that the taboo on killing them is not always matched by an obligation to feed them.

In *The Golden Bough* Sir James Frazer states that

> amongst the Todas, a pastoral people of the Nilgherry Hills of southern India, the dairy is a sanctuary, and the dairyman who attends to it has been described as a god. . . . Everyone, even his own father, prostrates himself before the milkman, and no one would dare to refuse him anything. No human being, except another milkman, may touch him; and he gives oracles to all who consult him, speaking with the voice of a god.

In the mythology of the Greeks, another Indo-European people, the bull was associated with the cult of Dionysus. That cult is supposed to have found its way to Greece, via Phoenicia, from the mountainous region on the frontiers of Persia and Asia Minor, very near to the realm of the Hittites.

Dionysus, another name for whom was Bacchus, was a god of fertility. According to the myth, he was the son of Zeus by his daughter Persephone. From the first he showed great promise but was attacked by the Titans, who were the enemies of the gods. Fleeing from them, he for a time eluded them by transforming himself into the shapes of various animals, but they caught up with him when he was in the shape of a bull, and cut him to pieces. In one version of the tale, the Titans dismembered him, boiled his limbs with herbs, and ate them. In due course, Dionysus rose again from the dead. According to some versions, the miracle was performed through the agency of his heart, which was the only part of him which survived. In another, his mangled limbs, not devoured by Titans, were recovered by his mother, or by one of the gods, and pieced together again.

As with almost all Greek gods, Dionysus had many aspects. He was the god of the vine, of the fig-tree, of the pine, and of the ivy. He was a god of agriculture, among his more popular emblems being the winnowing-fan. He was the god whom, unknowingly, twentieth-century merry-makers invoke when, in mid-winter, they perform the ancient ceremony of wassailing the apple trees. He was a horned god, having been born with horns. We see him, multiplied into many minor divinities, in the form of satyrs, fauns and tree-nymphs. He was the Great God Pan.

Above all, he was the god of vegetation and fertility. His death and subsequent resurrection are an allegory of the annual death each autumn of the crops of the earth and of the renewal of life each spring. It seemed logical to his worshippers to enact as far as possible the events of his life, death and revival at festivals in his honour. They were wild, licentious, "bacchanalian" affairs. In the Cretan version, and perhaps in others, the worshippers at the climax of the celebrations tore to pieces a live bull with

35

their teeth and ate his raw flesh. It was, from our viewpoint, a shocking performance.

Translated into Egyptian mythology, Dionysus became Osiris, concerning whom similar tales are told. The illegitimate son of the earth-god, Seb, and of the sky-goddess, Nut, he was hailed at his birth by a voice from heaven, announcing him as the Lord of All. Growing up to be a handsome lad, he first taught the Egyptians the arts of husbandry, showing them how to tend the vine, how to make wine from the grapes and how to cultivate wheat and barley. Later he travelled over all the Middle East, spreading his knowledge everywhere.

He had an enemy in his own family, his evil brother Set (who is identified with the Greek Typhon, chief of the Titans), who, by a trick, enticed him to creep into a wooden chest and then shut the lid on him. After sealing the coffer with molten lead, Set tossed it into the Nile. Osiris was, of course, drowned, and floated down to the sea and hence to Byblos, on the coast of Syria. Thither the coffer, now a coffin, was followed by Osiris's wife (and sister, for in good Egyptian tradition he married his sister), Isis. Numerous strange adventures occurred in Syria, culminating in Set, still pursuing his dead adversary, obtaining the corpse and cutting it into fourteen pieces.

Eventually, as in the story of Dionysus, Isis recovered the parts of the dismembered body and put them together. She fanned them with her wings, and lo! Osiris rose from the dead. Thereafter he became Lord of the Underworld, Lord of Eternity, promising to the faithful eternal life. And, as in Greece, his resurrection was celebrated by annual festivals intimately associated with agriculture.

Although he is so obviously identical with Dionysus, Osiris is not so closely associated with bulls. Perhaps that was because Egypt had another bull-god, Apis, though here mythology, as happens so often, becomes confused. Some accounts say that Osiris had two bulls, Apis and Mnevis, but in others he *is* one of the other of these bulls. As Apis belonged to the city of Memphis, and Mnevis to Heliopolis, the duality is explicable. Says Diodorus Siculus, the Roman historian who flourished in the first century B.C., "the sacred bulls, the one called Apis and the other Mnevis, were dedicated to Osiris, and it was ordained that they should be worshipped as gods in common by all the Egyptians, since these animals above all others had helped the discoverers of corn in sowing the seed and procuring the universal benefits of agriculture." Sir James Frazer adds, "although the bull Apis was worshipped as a god with much pomp and profound reverence, he was not suffered to live beyond a certain length of time which was prescribed by the sacred books, and on the expiry of which he was drowned in a holy spring. The limit, according to Plutarch, was twenty-five years; but it cannot always have been enforced, for the tombs of the Apis bulls have been discovered in modern times, and from the inscriptions on them it

36

appears that in the twenty-second dynasty two of the holy steers lived more than twenty-six years." It may be assumed that the word "steers" is loosely used and that "bulls" is intended. Incidentally, twenty-five or twenty-six years is a great age for a bull; few modern bulls live as long. The theory would seem to have been that the god, in this instance in the form of the bull Apis, must be put to death before his powers were exhausted, in order that he might be resurrected, presumably in the form of another and more virile bull, thus personifying the cycle of death and resurrection of vegetation.

As for Isis, in Egyptian art she is depicted as a cow, and even in human form she was usually adorned with horns. The cow was sacred to her.

To return to Greece for a moment, Zeus himself sometimes appeared in the form of a bull. And in Rome, Jupiter, the Roman form of Zeus, was offered a sacrifice of white oxen or bulls on Mount Alban and at the Capitol on certain festive occasions.

Mummified body of sacred bull calf, from Thebes, Egypt, about 1500 B.C.

Mention is made above of the Phoenician city of Byblos. This place was sacred to Adonis, or Tammuz, to give him his Semitic name, who has many points of similarity to Osiris and Dionysus. Like them, he is a god of vegetation. He is killed, in this instance by a wild boar, and then becomes the subject of contention between two goddesses, Persephone, queen of the Underworld, and Aphrodite, the goddess of love. Eventually they settle the tug-of-war by agreeing that Adonis shall spend half the year in the Underworld and half in the world of the living. When he returns, of course, for his six months in the sunlight the world bursts into new life and the season is one of rejoicing. Adonis and the two goddesses are found, under various names, in the mythologies of most of the ancient nations of the Middle East. Aphrodite is the Babylonian Ishtar, the Phoenician Astarte, and the Roman Venus. Persephone is the Chaldean Allatu. There is evidently some significance in the story that the coffin of Osiris should drift to Byblos, the Mediterranean centre of the Adonis cult.

Yet another god of the same family, about whom similar myths are told, was Attis, whose particular home seems to have been Phrygia, in Asia Minor. He too was a god of vegetation, who was killed and came back to life. His mother was Cybele, the Great Earth Mother and goddess of the beasts, who was worshipped throughout the Mediterranean world. One version of the death of Attis says that he was killed like Adonis, by a boar; another that he castrated himself under a pine tree. As with Adonis, two major festivals each year were held in honour of Attis, one commemorating his death, the other his resurrection. Both were distinguished by wild, hysterical scenes of savagery, in the course of which many men, swept away by emotion, voluntarily made themselves eunuchs – probably to their great regret when they came to their senses.

In addition to these public manifestations of reverence to Attis, the worship of the god developed a secret, esoteric aspect. Those worshippers who joined in the mourning for the dead god could, like him, rise again, through identification with him. As the bull was a sacred animal to Attis, this was accomplished by slaughtering a bull and washing the acolyte in his blood. Sir James Frazer describes the ceremony thus:

> In the baptism the devotee, crowned with gold and wreathed with fillets, descended into a pit, the mouth of which was covered with a wooden grating. A bull, adorned with garlands of flowers, its forehead glittering with gold leaf, was then driven on to the grating and there stabbed to death with a consecrated spear. Its hot, reeking blood poured in torrents through the apertures and was received with devout eagerness by the worshipper on every part of his person and garments, till he emerged from the pit,

drenched, dripping and scarlet from head to foot, to receive the homage, nay the adoration, of his fellows as one who has been born again to eternal life and had washed away his sins in the blood of the bull. For some time afterwards the fiction of a new birth was kept up by dieting him on milk, like a new-born babe. The regeneration of the worshipper took place at the same time as the regeneration of his god, namely, at the vernal equinox.

The cult of Attis and Cybele was transported to Rome in or about 205 B.C., when Hannibal was campaigning in Italy. Certain oracles revealed to the Romans that they might triumph over Hannibal if they would fetch from Phrygia a sacred black stone, evidently a meteorite, in which the goddess was supposed to reside. The stone was accordingly sent for and enshrined in a new temple on the Palatine Hill. When in due course the Roman armies defeated the Carthaginians, the goddess was given at least some of the credit, and for two hundred years her annual festivals were scrupulously observed, though elsewhere in the Roman Empire her worship was proscribed. Eventually in the reign of Claudius (41–54 A.D.) the prohibition was lifted, and thereafter the cult spread rapidly to many parts of the Empire. By this time, however, it seems to have become merged with the similar cult of Mithra.

Mithra was a Persian god. He is linked, though in exactly what way is not certain, with the great religious teacher, Zoroaster, who lived in north-western Iran in about the year 1000 B.C., according to some, in the sixth century B.C., according to others. He taught that life was an eternal conflict between good and evil, between light and darkness. Ahura-Mazda was the god of light, the personification of purity and goodness. Arrayed against him was Ahriman, the spirit of evil, the deceiver, the father of lies. Men have to choose between these two, and according to their choice so they will be rewarded in the eternal world to come.

Against the background of this lofty concept Mithra appears as a typical man-like hero. Born from solid rock, he is matched against various adversaries, typifying man's struggles against the forces of evil. First he wrestles with the Sun, whom he overcomes and who becomes his constant friend. Then he has to fight with the bull, the first living creature created by Ahura-Mazda.

In his epic struggle with the bull lies the heart of the Mithraic religion. First he captures the bull and takes it to the cave where he lives. Then it escapes and is recaptured and he is ordered to slay it. This he does not wish to do, so, when the time for the fatal stroke arrives, he turns his head as he plunges in the knife. At some time in the second century B.C. a sculptor in Asia Minor created a masterpiece of Mithra killing the bull, his head averted. It became a pattern for innumerable replicas. A sculptured representation of Mithra and the bull, at this same supreme moment, sat

Mithra slaying the bull by plunging his dagger into it while turning his head away. Typical Mithraic motif from sculpture of the 3rd century A.D. *found at Walbrook, London.*

on the altar-piece of every mithraeum, much as crucifixes are placed in Christian churches.

But the myth goes on to explain that the slaying of the bull was indeed necessary. Wherever his blood fell, grasses, flowers and corn sprang up with astonishing vigour. The bull was, in essence, the great creator from whose death sprang life.

During the period, up to 313 A.D., that Christianity was engaged in its great conflict with the State, Mithraism was one of its most formidable rivals. A mystery faith, it offered a ritual cleansing from sin, a new life and immortality. Many of its ceremonies were borrowed from the cult of Cybele and Attis. Initiates went through the ceremony of the taurobolium, in which, descending into a grave-like recess under a grating, they were washed in the blood of the bull and emerged to new life. Christians retorted that they were washed, spiritually though not actually, in the blood of the Lamb, as in the Epistle to the Hebrews (chapter 9) which argues that "if the blood of goats and bulls and the sprinkled ashes of a heifer have power to hallow those who have been defiled and restore their external purity, how much greater is the power of the blood of Christ . . ." Later in the same letter the writer asserts that "sins can never be removed by the blood of bulls and goats".

It is interesting to reflect that the cult of voodoo, which in some of its features bears a striking resemblance to Mithraism, flourishes in Caribbean and other Latin American countries where bull-fighting has also become established. Not that the voodoo initiate is washed in the blood of the bull – that would be far too expensive; but he *is* washed in the blood of a cock or a goat. He does descend into a symbolic tomb or womb for the washing and emerges, cleansed from sin, to a new life. The rebirth is so complete that he is given a new name, by which he must always be referred to, and every effort is made to obliterate his former identity.

In Asia Minor, adjoining the ancient land of Phrygia, home of Attis, was the province of Galatia, which was inhabited by a Celtic people who had somehow become detached from the main body of Celts during their westward migrations around the middle of the first millenium B.C. Among the Celtic personal names recorded fairly frequently in Galatia is Deiotaros, which means Divine Bull. Oak trees were common objects of veneration throughout Europe, being often associated with Zeus or Jupiter, who was also a god of thunder and sometimes took the form of a bull. It is not therefore surprising to hear of "bull oaks". Several such were, or still are, to be found in the British Isles, where the popular explanation of the name is that they were hollow oaks with a big enough cavity to shelter bulls. It is significant, however, that many of them have stories of hauntings and similar uncanny happenings attached to them. One in Windsor Forest was haunted by the ghost of a mysterious character named Herne the Hunter, who, according to some authorities, was a British form of the Celtic god Cernunnos, known chiefly in Gaul. Both Cernunnos and Herne the Hunter are said to have been horned, though the legend attached to Herne gives him stag's antlers. Some think that the naked and virile giant carved on the chalk hillside above Cerne Abbas, in Dorset, is really Cernunnos.

The Celtic druids, when cutting the sacred mistletoe from oak trees with a golden sickle, used to sacrifice two white bulls, apparently as a propitiation to the god of the oak. It seems that the glutinous mistletoe berries were regarded as the semen of the oak-tree god, so what more appropriate than to offer as compensation two of the most sexually potent of animals?

Another horned Celtic god was the giant Benlli, who is remembered in the unlikely guise of the nursery-rhyme character, "Robin the Bobbin, the big-bellied Ben, who ate more meat than four-score men". The beef he devoured probably represents cattle sacrificed to him, and it is recorded that bullocks were sacrificed to an obscure saint, St. Beyno, who is probably Benlli in another disguise, as late as 1589. There are references to cattle being burnt alive as sacrifices to avert cattle disease in remote corners of the British Isles (such as Cornwall and the Hebrides) even in the eighteenth and nineteenth centuries.

Bulls were also used by the Irish Celts for soothsaying. G. Keating (*General History of Ireland*) says that the Druids "slew a bull and spread out its hide on round wattles made of the quicken tree, putting the side that had been next to the flesh uppermost". Apparently the seer then slept on the hide, prophesying according to his dreams. This custom was also observed in the Highlands of Scotland. The sacrifice of a bull was also the prerequisite for the choosing of a king in old Ireland. When the clans were assembled at Tara, a chief druid slaughtered a bull, ate a heavy meal of its flesh and then forced himself into an hypnotic trance, in the course of which he was given clues to the identity of the chieftain who must be selected. The ceremony was called *tardfeis*, which means "bull-dream". In another Irish myth, it is the druid himself who is sacrificed, though for the purpose he had taken the form of a cow.

Sir James Frazer examines this aspect of bull sacrifice in the context of the "bouphonia", an Athenian festival held at about the time of the threshing of the harvest. The bull (the author calls it an ox, but in many instances he seems to use the words "bull", "ox" and "steer" indiscriminately) was slain with an intricate ritual, in which everyone who participated endeavoured to remain anonymous and to throw the blame for his actions on someone else. Thus, the butchers blamed the men who gave them axe and knife, those men blamed the men who had sharpened the weapons, and those men blamed the girls who poured water on the whetstone, and so on. This, says Sir James, suggests that the killing was originally regarded as murder, the animal being considered an incarnate god.

He gives further instances of bull sacrifice, as among the Slavs and in ancient China. In the latter country it seems that the bull was associated with the corn-spirit, as it was in Greece. Sacrifices were made at the beginning of the Chinese New Year by a person known as the Divine Husbandman, who wore a bull mask on the body of a man. Many of the examples he quotes were from central Europe, where the last

Chariot pole end in form of a bull's head, from Chin-ts'un, China, 5th to 4th century, B.C. *It is of bronze, inlaid with gold and silver.*

stalks of corn at harvest were fashioned into the shape of a bull with horns, as in England they are still woven into the shape of a corn goddess, or kern baby. In some regions of Europe, this effigy was known as The Bull. In others, the title was given to the man who made the last stroke with his scythe or sickle. In several districts of France a bull was slain and eaten with considerable ceremony at the end of harvest. Other places were content with a calf.

Mention of the Chinese bull-mask serves to remind us that similar masks were once widely used in England. Until the beginning of the present century one still survived at Melbury Osmond, in Dorset, and in earlier times it seems likely that many Dorset villages had similar masks. Shillingstone, in the same county, possessed one which was worn by a man who took it into the streets at Christmas, pouncing on people and demanding refreshments. At Shillingstone it was known as the "Christmas Bull", but the more general term was "The Ooser". Nor was it confined to Dorset. I remember the term being used, when I was a small boy, as a kind of bogey-man to frighten recalcitrant children in my village in south Wiltshire – "The Ooser'll have ee!" There is a suspicious resemblance to The Ooser mask in the head of The Giant, an effigy kept in Salisbury Museum for parading the streets of the city on festival days, and in the mask of the Padstow Obby Oss, who appears on May Day.

Echoes of bull-worship and perhaps bull sacrifice may be detected in a verse

43

chanted in the Horn Ceremony held, until about 1890, at the fair at Weyhill, Hampshire, which had been held from time immemorial at a spot where two ancient ways cross.

> Swift is the hare; cunning is the fox;
> Why should not this little calf grow up to be an ox?
> To get his own living, among the briars and thorns,
> And die like his daddy, with a great pair of horns.

The song was known to shepherds and drovers for miles around and was quoted to me by an old uncle, a shepherd, in the 1920s. Members of Hampshire Women's Institutes collected in the 1930s (and published in their book, *It Happened in Hampshire*) a few further facts about the Weyhill celebration. According to one version a pair of horns was placed in turn on the heads of newcomers to the Fair. In another, "the newcomer was seated in a chair, and a hat adorned with a pair of horns and a cup were placed on his head." The initiate drank ale from the cup and then paid for drinks all round!

Sumerian copper figure of a bison, from Van, Turkey, about 2300 B.C.

The line about dying like his daddy, with a great pair of horns, is suggestive.

Readers familiar with the Bible will know where to find many Old Testament references to bulls. Jehovah (Yahweh), the god of the early Hebrews, is supposed by some authorities to have originally been a bull god, and some of the instructions for religious ritual, recorded in the books of Exodus and Leviticus, relate specifically to bulls. For example, the procedure for installing Aaron as high-priest, according to Exodus, chapter 29 (*New English Bible*), includes the following:

> Next you shall install Aaron and his sons. Bring the bull to the front of the Tent of the Presence, and they shall lay their hands on its head. Slaughter the bull before the Lord at the entrance to the Tent of the Presence. Take some of its blood, and put it with your finger on the horns of the altar. Pour all the rest of it at the base of the altar. Then take the fat covering the entrails, the long lobe of the liver, and the two kidneys with the fat upon them, and burn it on the altar; but the flesh of the bull, and its skin and offal, you shall destroy by fire outside the camp. It is a sin-offering.

Later in the same chapter, when it is stated that the installation ceremonies are to last seven days, there occurs the further instruction – "Offer a bull daily, a sin-offering as expiation for sin."

The Book of Leviticus (chapter 4) goes into similiar but even greater detail and there follow similar instructions for the ritual if (a) "a man of standing" commits an inadvertent sin, and (b) if "the whole community of Israel sins inadvertently". In a later chapter (16) is an account of how Aaron, the high priest, offered such as offering for the sins of his two sons. The general procedure was the same but there are one or two interesting differences in detail.

In the Book of Numbers the Moabite prophet, Balaam, is said to have offered seven bulls as a preliminary to his pronouncing a curse on the Israelites. And when the Israelites were camping on the plains of Moab, preparatory to entering the Promised Land of Canaan, the instructions given for burnt offerings represent a veritable holocaust of domestic animals. In addition to the offerings for offences, two young bulls (and other animals) had to be slaughtered on the first day of every month. Two young bulls also on the festival of the Passover and on the festival of Firstfruits. In the seventh month occurred a whole week of holiday and religious ceremonies, starting on the fifteenth day of the month. On the first day of this festival thirteen young bulls were sacrificed; on the second day, twelve; on the third day, eleven; on the fourth day, ten; on the fifth day, nine; on the sixth day, eight; on the seventh day, seven; and finally, to conclude the celebrations, on the eighth day, one.

The Israelites must have been very rich on cattle if they could sustain this output for long. But apparently they did, for in the Second Book of Chronicles (chapter 30) is an account of King Hezekiah's restoration of the traditional religion, in which occurs the detail that a thousand bulls (and seven thousand sheep) were set aside for sacrifice during a week of rejoicing.

In the Psalms, too, and in the Book of Isaiah, are references to sacrifices of bulls, as where the Lord is made to say, "I need take no young bull from your house . . . for all the beasts of the forest are mine and the cattle in thousands upon my hills." Or as when, in the Book of Isaiah (chapter 1), the Lord chides the Israelites, "I am sated with the whole offerings of rams and the fat of buffaloes. I have no desire for the blood of bulls, of sheep and of he-goats. Whenever you come to enter my presence – who asked you for this?"

Several of the words translated as "calf" in the Authorized Version of the Bible are corrected to "bull-calf" in the *New English Bible*. Thus, the golden image that Aaron set up for the Israelites to worship while Moses was on Mount Sinai becomes a bull-calf. And, although in the First Book of Kings (chapter 12) the golden god which Jeroboam set up when he rebelled against the government in Jerusalem remains a calf, there can be little doubt that it followed the convention and was a bull-calf.

For bull worship was endemic throughout the Middle East. The descriptions of ceremonies and rituals for sacrifices preserved in the Old Testament are examples, for which we should be grateful, of a tradition that must have been widespread. The Bible itself refers to bull worship and calf-worship in neighbouring states – "Your calf-god stinks, O Samaria; my anger flares against them . . . For what sort of god is this bull?"

In Babylon the bull was the symbol or incarnation of Adad, the god of lightning. Assyrian sculptures abound in representations of winged bulls. Ante-dating both Babylonia and Assyria, Ur of the Chaldees, the city of Abraham in the land of Sumer, also had its sacred bulls.

Among the tombs discovered in Ur by Sir Leonard Woolley was one of a wealthy lady named Shub-ad, and another, nearby, of a man named A-bar-gi, who was possibly her husband. Shub-ad, dressed in all her finery, had been taken to her grave on a sledge drawn by asses; A-bar-gi in an ox-drawn waggon. The animals and a large number of human attendants were then interred in the same graves (Shub-ad

(Right) *Bulls, the symbols of the lightning god, Adad, on the Ishtar Gate, Babylon. 605–563* B.C.

had 25; A-bar-gi 65). Shub-ad's attendants were, naturally, all female and were attired in what was apparently their court regalia. They wore necklaces of gold and lapis-lazuli, great ear-rings like crescent moons, ribbons of silver and gold in their hair and red cloaks with decorated cuffs. The fact that they all lay tranquilly in rows suggests that they were drugged before interment. Some of the girls were harpists, and the instruments which they still held in their hands were shaped like a bull, culminating in a bull's head in gold, bearing a beard of lapis-lazuli (see opposite page 33). This was the bull-god of the Sumerians, known to them as Dumuzi and in other parts of the Near East as Tammuz. It was his voice, presumably accompanied by music from the harps, that had summoned A-bar-gi and Shub-ad to a new life after death. Dumuzi had a death-and-resurrection festival which corresponded in date to the subsequent Hebrew Passover and the Christian Easter.

A further twist to the story is provided by the apparent fact that A-bar-gi was a god-king who was ritually slain at the end of his term of office. The idea thus demonstrated that a king must die at the height of his powers in order to make way for a younger and vigorous successor is, as we have noted, extremely widespread and very ancient. And it is paralleled in the wild herd by the old dominant bull who, when his strength begins to decline, is quickly ousted by a younger successor.

Linked with it is the notion of sympathetic magic. To stimulate the earth to bring forth bountiful crops from the seed deposited in it, the example of human beings demonstrating what ought to be done was helpful, perhaps essential. Hence the happy pilgrimage of young men and girls into the greenwood on a night in early spring – a custom remembered, if not actually perpetuated, by our May Day celebrations. To perform as energetically as the gods required demanded a leader in the prime of life. And, by analogy, what was more natural than to regard this dominant individual as an incarnation of that most potent of all masculine animals, the bull.

4
Sport with Bulls in the Ancient World

From the account of bull-gods in the previous chapter one country, Crete, has been deliberately excluded. The reason for doing so is that, although in ancient Crete a bull cult arose in much the same manner as in most other countries of the Mediterranean and the Middle East, here it developed rather differently.

Crete, southernmost and largest of the Greek islands, is situated in mid-Mediterranean about seventy miles south of the southernmost point of mainland Greece and roughly equidistant from Europe, Asia and Africa. We now know that it was the home of one of the earliest and most brilliant of ancient civilizations, but until Sir Arthur Evans started excavating there in 1899 almost nothing was known about that remote period. Modern research has shown that a splendid kingdom had become established there by about 1900 B.C. and endured till at least 1400. Its chief city was Knossos, which at one time had an estimated population of 100,000. Its people were sophisticated and gay, the fashionable women wearing dresses that look surprisingly modern. Literacy was widespread.

The Minoan civilization of Crete, as it is called from one of its most powerful kings, Minos, foundered as a result of a natural disaster in about the year 1400. Vigorous warrior tribes from mainland Greece took advantage of the opportunity to supplant the Cretan rulers and glorify their own kingdom, based on Mycenae. In time the Mycenean civilization also collapsed, to be replaced by new nations and empires, till even the memory of Knossos was buried as deep as its walls and palaces were beneath the accumulating soil.

What survived were certain vague legends of a magnificent city which had existed in the now eroded island at the dawn of time. According to Greek mythology, Zeus, their principal god, was born in Crete. His mother Rhea had taken refuge there because her husband, Cronos, had the unpleasant habit of devouring his own children as soon as they were born.

Bulls were pursued for sport in ancient times, as is shown in this Assyrian stone frieze from Nimrud. 9th century B.C.

A little later Minos, who is said to have been a son of Zeus, became king of Crete. He conducted a war against Athens, was victorious, and demanded as tribute an annual shipment of twelve noble youths and maidens, to be sacrificed to the Minotaur in Knossos.

This is where the Cretan bull comes into the story. It seems that Minos had a nymphomaniac queen, Pasiphae, who conceived the idea that she wanted to be raped by a bull. A skilled Cretan engineer and mathematician, Daedalus, fashioned for Pasiphae the model of a cow, into which she could creep for the purpose she had in mind. In due course she was satisfied, and the progeny of her mating was a bull-headed monster who came to be known as the Minotaur.

The Minotaur lived in a vast region of passages and corridors beneath the great palace of Knossos. Into it every year were introduced the twelve victims from Athens, who were left to wander around hopelessly, looking for a way of escape, until the Minotaur pounced on and ate them. Assuredly a bedtime story to scare Greek children.

The Minotaur's reign of terror came to an end with the arrival of Theseus, son of the Athenian king. With this handsome youth Ariadne, the daughter of King Minos, fell in love, so when it was his turn to enter the labyrinth she provided him with a reel of thread. With the aid of this he was able to find his way about the maze. He slew the Minotaur, emerged from the labyrinth and, meeting Ariadne by previous arrangement, set sail by night and so escaped to Athens.

Such was the myth in which the classical Greeks incorporated virtually all they knew about ancient Crete. As usual with myths, it embodied a germ of truth, which modern research has been able to extract. The key to it is the special relationship of the bull to Crete.

On the walls of the royal palace of Knossos are vivid paintings of acrobats doing incredible feats with bulls. They are depicted as grasping the huge horns from the front, somersaulting over the animal's back and landing gracefully on their feet at his rear. In one painting a boy is shown in mid-air, while a girl, behind the animal, waits to steady the acrobat as he comes to earth. A second girl is preparing to follow the boy. One horn is under her left armpit, and she is getting a good grip in readiness for a backward somersault (see colour plate opposite page 64). There can be little doubt that "bull-leaping" of this kind, fantastic though it appears, was actually performed. Probably the boys and girls required as annual tribute from Athens were destined for training for the Cretan bull ring.

There has been much controversy about these murals. Some authorities have maintained that the feat shown is impossible, commenting that a charging bull tends to throw his head about, in an attempt to gore his adversary. Others say it can be done. In all probability there were many casualties among the Cretan acrobats. (But see also Chapter 7.)

Although held in an arena, Cretan "bull-leaping" had apparently to be regarded as a ritual rather than as a sport. There are representations of bulls by the hundreds and thousands in Knossos. They are on murals and frescoes, on seals and signet rings, in statues and bas-relief. There are also dark crypts in which evidently bulls were sacrificed. In the foundations of one building were found, set against corner stones, the heads of "two large oxen of the Urus breed, the horn cores of one of which were over a foot in girth at the base".

But the principal deity of Crete was not a bull but the Great Mother Goddess, worshipped by the Greeks as Cybele. Doubtless it was to her that the bulls were sacrificed, and to her, too, that the dangerous "bull-leaping" was dedicated. The observant Sir Arthur Evans had at Knossos an experience which immediately suggested to him a link between the Goddess and the bulls.

One June evening during the course of his excavations he was lying on his bed in the basement of his headquarters building when earth tremors began. They lasted for about a minute-and-a-half. The earth shook and vibrated, producing, he said, the same physical effect as a rough sea and at the same time emitting a sound *"like the muffled roar of a bull"*. Crete is, of course, situated in one of the major earthquake zones of the world. Quite a number of tremors have been recorded within historic times.

In the Minoan period her people developed a sea empire so powerful that it dominated the whole of the eastern Mediterranean. Its colonies and ports were found on many of the Greek islands, even within a few miles of Athens, and apparently as far west as Sicily. In the east it traded with ports on the coast of Syria and Asia Minor and with Egypt. Only a strong naval power could have hoped to invade the island, and at the time of its collapse it seems to have been as prosperous as ever. The inhabitants lived in peace among their vineyards and gardens and olive groves, seeing no necessity for fortifying their coast against enemies. Why, then, was it overwhelmed by disaster?

One suspicion is that the subterranean bull stirred, and tossed his head. A more

Clay figure of bull from Psyrra, Crete, about 1500 B.C.

Scenes from an ancient Greek bowl depicting the deeds of Theseus. On the right he is capturing a bull single-handed.

recent theory, almost certainly correct, is that it was devastated as the result of a prodigious volcanic eruption on the island of Thera, the southernmost of the Cyclades islands, due north of central Crete. At a time which has been dated by the latest scientific methods as within a few years of 1500 B.C. a previously extinct volcano on the island erupted violently. Accompanying this eruption were earthquakes which caused some damage on Crete. A period of quiescence of perhaps 20 or 30 years followed, to be interrupted by an even more tremendous explosion. The island of Thera blew up, with a force approached though probably not equalled in historic times only by the eruption of the island of Krakatoa, in the East Indies, in 1883. Only fragments of Thera remained, the former centre of the island being submerged in deep water, and such buildings of the Minoans as remained were buried under volcanic debris in places up to 66 metres thick.

There are references in the records of antiquity to "the bull from the sea". This, say some modern authorities, was a *tsunami*, or tidal wave, which follows an earthquake or eruption. The *tsunami*, caused by the destruction of Thera, hit the north coast of Crete with tremendous force and a roar like the bellowing of a mighty bull. That is what caused the indescribable havoc which ruined the Minoan empire.

53

In the light of recent archaeological work on Thera, the island, together with the Minoan civilization of Crete, has been tentatively but convincingly identified by certain scholars with the lost Atlantis. It is worth remembering that Plato's account of Atlantis, which is our chief source of information, came to him in the form of an ancient tradition from an Egyptian source. From Egypt the island of Crete is almost due west, and the story of Atlantis is about a land to the west.

As happened with Krakatoa in 1883, the island of Thera literally exploded, at a date somewhere between 1500 and 1470 B.C. The wealthy Minoan settlement on the island itself was entirely obliterated, while Crete was wrecked by the tidal wave, by the accompanying earth paroxysms and by the fall-out of ash. The casualties must have been enormous, and the survivors were doubtless panic-stricken and defence-less. When the realization of what had happened penetrated mainland Greece, no doubt the more primitive peoples there sailed out to the islands and took possession. In spite of the propitiary sacrifices and the long-continued ritual of the bull ring, the "bull from the sea" had broken loose and had destroyed the Minoan empire.

If Crete and Thera are thus correctly identified as Atlantis, we have in Plato's description of that island a wonderful picture of Minoan Crete in its golden age. His accounts in *Timaeus* and *Critias* are far too long to be quoted here, but the place seems to have been an earthly paradise, abounding in fruits and crops of all kinds, in flowers, trees, wild and domestic animals (including many elephants) and magnificent buildings and palaces. Considerable emphasis is naturally laid on its harbours and ships. However, let us content ourselves with the references to bulls.

There were ten independent kings ruling in the island, each with complete jurisdiction over his own territory but having mutual and peaceable relations with his neighbours "regulated by the commands of Poseidon which the law had handed down. These were inscribed by the first kings on a pillar of orichalcum, which was situated in the middle of the island, at the temple of Poseidon, whither the kings gathered together every fifth and every sixth year alternately". Plato then describes the procedure:

> And when they were gathered together they consulted about their common interests, and inquired if anyone had transgressed in anything, and passed judgment, and before passing judgment they gave their pledges to one another on this wise:
>
> There were bulls who had the range of the temple of Poseidon; and the ten kings, being left alone in the temple, after they had offered prayers to the god that they might capture the victim which was acceptable to him, hunted the bulls, without weapons, but with staves and nooses; and the bull which they caught they led up to the pillar and cut its throat over the top of it so that the blood fell upon the sacred inscription. Now on

*Embossed designs on gold cups from a tomb at Vapheio, Sparta, Greece, of about 1500 B.C.
(Left) A bull charging two figures, one of whom clings to his horns while the other sprawls on
the ground. (Right) A cow, with tail slightly raised, enticing a bull.*

the pillar, besides the laws, there was inscribed an oath invoking mighty curses on the
disobedient. When therefore, after slaying the bull in the accustomed manner, they
proceeded to burn its limbs, they filled a bowl of wine and cast in a clot of blood for each
of them; the rest of the victim they put in the fire, after having purified the column all
round. Then they drew from the bowl in golden cups, and, pouring a libation on the
fire, they swore that they would judge according to the laws on the pillar.

Some years before Sir Arthur Evans began his excavations at Knossos two gold
cups with splendid engravings were found at Vapheio, in mainland Greece. They are
of Minoan craftsmanship and were probably imported from Crete. The scenes
portrayed are of the capture of bulls and are of considerable interest in view of the
statement in Plato's account that the Atlantean bulls were taken by men with no
weapons but staves and nooses. In one of them it is clear that the hunters were using a
sexually receptive cow as a decoy. The cow has her tail slightly raised and is turning
her head to look with interest at the bull. The bull himself is so preoccupied with her
that he fails to notice the hunters creeping up and slipping a lasso around his hind leg.

On the other cup are scenes of a bull hunt in which Minoan youths *and* girls are
endeavouring to catch a bull in a net stretched between two trees. In one scene a bull
is trapped, but in another he is free and has tossed one hunter, who lies on the ground.
Another hunter, a girl, has grasped the bull by the horns and is wrestling with him
presumably in an attempt to protect her fallen companion. She has wrapped herself

55

around the bull's head and clings to it so closely that it is impossible for the animal to gore her.

The bulls in every instance are huge wild ones, of aurochs type. Those portrayed in the murals of Knossos stand, by comparison with the acrobats, six or more feet at the shoulders and have a length of eight or nine feet. They are massive creatures, with rather short legs, and are coloured pied or brindled, with the distinctive finching spinal stripe.

*　　　*　　　*

Apparently no direct link exists between the arena of Knossos and those of Rome. Chronologically, the gap is one of more than a thousand years. Nor is there much real resemblance between what went on in them. The bull-leaping of Minoan Crete, spectacular though it must have been, was primarily a religious ritual. The Roman "games" degenerated into lavish and bloodthirsty spectacles designed to pander to the worst instincts of the most depraved sections of the population. They had no excuse and no meaning; their sole purpose was to cater for a lust for blood and cruelty.

Rhyton vase terminating in a bull's head; from Ruvo, Italy, about 400–350 B.C.

Probably the Roman games originated with the customary attractions at country fairs. Throughout the world these have always been occasions for sport and entertainment. They provided an opportunity for country folk, who otherwise spent their lives in relative isolation on farms, to meet each other, enjoy a few convivial drinks and take any opportunities for showing off their skill, strength or wealth. As late as the nineteenth century shepherds of southern England, who at other seasons led the loneliest of lives, engaged in combats for the title "King of the Shepherds" when they met at autumn sheep fairs. John Stow, writing of London in the year 1598, records that on summer holiday occasions "the youths are exercised in leaping, dancing, shooting, wrestling, casting the stone, and practising their shields; the maidens trip in their timbrels, and dance as long as they can well see. In winter . . . the boars prepared for brawn are set to fight, or else bulls and bears are baited."

Much the same must have happened in the early days, when Rome was a market town.

Unhappily Rome had a custom which set it several degrees lower than even the somewhat coarse and brutal Elizabethan era in the scale of human excellence. It was based on slavery, and it treated its slaves, in general, with complete callousness. One day, in the third century B.C., two brothers, seeking to honour their recently deceased father, hit on the idea of setting a few slaves to fight to the death over his grave. As slaves were valuable this was quite a pecuniary sacrifice on their part, and it gave them a chance, for doubtless there was a funeral oration, to draw attention to the superior qualities of the dead man. The fight was a wild success, great crowds coming to watch. Thereafter, anyone seeking popularity, and particularly aspiring politicians, staged slave fights. And as everyone tried to outdo his rivals, the contests became more and more lavish. Entrepreneurs thought nothing of putting scores of pairs of slaves to fight in public squares or market-places. A class of merchant arose which bought, trained and sold slaves for the purpose, the trained slaves being known as gladiators.

Against such duels the older sports of the fair, such as juggling, wrestling, acrobatic displays and the less bloodthirsty sports, seemed tame. Nevertheless, animals are always an attraction, and the Romans had no inhibitions about how they were treated. As an alternative to gladiator fights the promoters staged animal fights, sometimes matching unlike animals against each other, such as tigers against wolves, or alternatively setting the animals to oppose men. In later times the animal shows in the arenas often became a free-for-all. Daniel P. Mannix, who has collected a great number of facts about the games in *Those About to Die* describes wild beast hunts in the Colosseum and says that the number and variety of animals presented was astonish-

A Roman bull about to be sacrificed.

ing. Commenting on one such hunt in the reign of Domitian (81–96 A.D.), he writes:

> Martial says that there were nine thousand animals killed in these six-day games. There were deer, wild boars, bears, bulls, antelopes, ibex, jackals, ostriches, cranes, wild horses, hyenas, leopards, and a herd of domestic cattle put in for "padding". The whole arena seemed covered with a patchwork quilt of various coloured skins. Fights were constantly breaking out, but the arena was so crowded and the animals so terrified that by mere weight of numbers the contestants were jostled apart and swept away from each other as the frantic creatures tried to find some way to escape.

The deserts, forests and jungles of Africa and Asia, and the woods and mountains of northern Europe, were combed for more and yet more animals to be slaughtered in the arenas not only of Rome but of provincial towns within the Empire. The rot spread to every city, from Mesopotamia to Spain. The games, too, took a heavy toll of human life. Julius Caesar, who was responsible for first staging games in the arena on such a colossal scale, had the bright idea of using the occasion for testing out new weapons and methods of warfare. He set captive soldiers from the distant regions of the known world to fight each other, each with his own national weapons, while Caesar watched with professional interest, to detect which if any of them offered advantages over the conventional ones. Such immense spectacles, too, called for complex stage management and timing, and involved much training. Most of the great cats, for instance, will not willingly attack and eat men and had to be trained on a diet of human flesh before they could be trusted to attack their quarry in the arena. A lion might have to undergo a training of many weeks, using slaves with their arms bound or broken for his meals. Very large numbers of human beings were thus required for service in the lairs of the wild beasts behind the scenes, as well as those who actually appeared in the arena. It became the custom to use convicts for the purpose, and, so great was the demand, the sentence "to the arena" became one of the commonest of punishments in the law courts.

With so much going on in the arena when the games were in progress, the role of bulls became a relatively minor one. But they were part of the basic stock attractions. There were usually bulls around, though in competition with such exotic fauna as hippopotami, crocodiles, giraffes and oryx they attracted less attention than they would otherwise have done. There are incidental references to them in some contemporary accounts of the shows. Mannix says, "Acrobatic troupes of men and women learned how to grab a charging bull by the horns and turn somersaults over its back." This, of course, if true, parallels the achievements of the Cretan acrobats.

Mannix describes how the Colosseum was covered by an enormous awning, to shield the audience from the sun, and he mentions that "ancient writers talk of naked little boys with wings tied to them to represent cupids being swung back and forth across the arena by invisible wires, as though they were flying." Then he adds, "Often large animals, in one case a bull, were carried up to the awning (which was painted to represent the sky) by invisible wires to illustrate some mythological incident."

Mannix devotes much of the eleventh chapter of his book to an account of a bull fight in the arena. A considerable number of animals of three species, the aurochs, the European bison and the musk ox, were driven into the arena together. At first they stood in the centre of the arena, taking stock of the situation, so dummies were thrown to them, to play with. Then acrobatic attendants known as dodgers came to tease them, flipping a bull's tail and then darting to safety behind a barrier. The animals started to warm up, and some began to fight each other.

At some stage of the programme a troupe of bull-leapers put on a performance.

Mannix comments that although much doubt is cast on the ability of Cretans to manage this feat, there are also Roman murals depicting it. Apparently one man distracts the bull's attention while another runs forward, grabs the bull's horns and places his feet on the bull's forehead. The bull automatically tosses his head, which throws the acrobat into the air. He turns a somersault in the air, lands lightly on the bull's back and immediately slides off over his tail. Meantime his companions are keeping the bull fully occupied, encouraging him to charge them rather than the tumbler who is in the air. In some versions apparently the acrobat turns a back somersault and is caught as he lands by a couple of his assistants.

When the bulls were thoroughly incensed, the condemned criminals whom they were to kill were herded in. This part of the proceedings was perhaps the item which the audience liked best, though one of the roles of the victims was to give the bulls new confidence to face their final ordeal in a proper pugnacious mood.

When the criminals had been despatched, there were more acts by tumblers and dodgers, including some by professional bull-wrestlers, who seized a bull by the horns and threw them – a feat which is still performed in rodeos (see page 88).

Finally, the *venators*, or hunters, who were to fight with the bulls to the death, entered, bearing sword and cape, as modern bullfighters do. But apparently not all the bulls were killed, for there are references to bulls who had been in the ring many times getting wise to the procedures and proving more than a match for their tormentors.

*   *   *

In the first three centuries A.D. the criminals punished in the arenas included many Christians, and we have several graphic accounts of the experiences of those who suffered in that way. Perhaps the most poignant and revealing of all is the story of Perpetua and Felicitas, two girls of Thuburbo, in North Africa, whose martyrdom is thought to have occurred in A.D. 203.

Perpetua was a member of a well-to-do family; Felicitas was her personal serving-maid or slave-girl. Not long before her arrest Perpetua, who is said to have been aged 22, had given birth to a son; Felicitas was eight months pregnant and was delivered of a daughter in prison. Both were catechumens, i.e., they had decided to become Christians and were under instruction before baptism, which took place, in fact, after they had been arrested. The story is the more remarkable in that the first part of it is a first-hand account, written by Perpetua herself while in prison. It reveals her anxiety for her small son, her compassion for her father who was overcome by grief, her light-

Two Roman gladiators fighting a bull.

hearted almost gay approach to death, and her incredible courage. Their appearance in the arena is set down by an eye-witness.

The day of their victory dawned, and they marched from the prison to the amphitheatre joyfully as though they were going to heaven, with calm faces, trembling, if at all, with joy rather than fear. Perpetua went along with shining countenance and calm step, as the beloved of God, as a wife of Christ, putting down everyone's stare by her own intense gaze. With them also was Felicitas, glad that she had safely given birth so that now she could fight the beasts . . .

The proceedings began.

Saturninus and Revocatus were matched with a leopard, and then while in the stocks they were attacked by a bear. As for Saturninus, he dreaded nothing more than a bear, and he counted on being killed by one bite of a leopard. Then he was matched with a wild boar; but the gladiator who had tied him to the animal was gored by the boar and died a few days after the contest, whereas Saturninus was only dragged along. Then when he was bound in the stocks awaiting the bear, the animal refused to come out of the cages, so that Saturninus was called back once more unhurt.

For the young women, however, the Devil had prepared a mad heifer. This was an unusual animal, but it was chosen that their sex might be matched with that of the beast. So they were stripped naked, placed in nets and thus brought out into the arena. Even the crowd was horrified when they saw that one was a delicate young girl and the other a woman fresh from child-birth, with the milk still dripping from her breasts. And so they were brought back again and dressed in their unbelted tunics.

First the heifer tossed Perpetua and she fell on her back. Then sitting up she pulled down the tunic that was ripped along the side so that it covered her thighs, thinking more of her modesty than of her pain. Next she asked for a pin to fasten her untidy hair; for it was not right that a martyr should die with her hair in disorder, lest she might seem to be mourning in her hour of triumph.

Then she got up. And seeing that Felicitas had been crushed to the ground, she went over to her, gave her her hand, and lifted her up. Then the two stood side by side. But the cruelty of the mob was now appeased, and so they were called back through the Gate of Life (by which those who had survived left the arena).

There Perpetua was held up by a man named Rusticus who was at the time a catechumen and kept close to her. She awoke from a kind of sleep . . . and she began to look about her. Then to the amazement of all she said: "When are we going to be thrown to that heifer or whatever it is?"

When told that this had already happened, she refused to believe it until she noticed the marks of her rough experience on her person and dress . . .

But the death verdict on the Christians had not yet been implemented. Some had died, but some were still alive and had to be despatched. They had been thrown to wild beasts and survived, so there was to be no more torture. They had to go "to the usual spot" to have their throats cut.

Although in this instance the animal involved in the drama was a heifer, not a bull, the narrative illustrates graphically events in a Roman arena, from the viewpoint of some of the participants.

5

Bull-baiting
and Bull-fighting

The supposition that the Spanish bullfight is the direct development of the bull-fights staged in Roman arenas is a natural one. It is not necessarily correct. Some researchers into the subject have produced a different explanation of its origins.

Bulls being driven into a town for a market or fair are natural targets for rough sport. It happens even today, as in the streets of Pamplona. What more natural, too, that, as a climax to the wild career of bulls and men through the streets and lanes to the market square, the local count, duke, lord or whatever he was called, should arrive on horseback and display his prowess by delivering the *coup de grâce*. This, according to one school of thought, was the origin of the picador.

But as the centuries passed and the gap between the aristocracy and the common herd grew wider, it was considered beneath the dignity of the great man to act as common butcher. He fought with and subdued the bull, but left the final business to one of his servants. This man, the matador or killer of the bull, eventually became the central figure in the drama. The man on the horse, the picador, now occupies a subsidiary role and is often a figure of derision.

John Marks (*To The Bullfight Again*) says that there is no evidence that the Visigoths, who invaded and occupied Spain in 466 A.D., had any interest in bull-fighting, or at least in the sort of bull-fights staged in arenas. Nor, when they replaced the Visigoths in the decades following 711 A.D., did the Moors. So, as the Visigoths and Moors between them dominated Spain for the best part of five hundred years, there is a large gap between the shows in the Roman amphitheatres and the later Spanish cult of the bull-fight. But, of course, we do not know whether games in the arenas continued as purely plebeian attractions, in spite of the disapproval or indifference of the new ruling classes.

On their take-over in Spain, John Marks comments,

> the Moors promptly adopted the original Iberian version of bull-worship, which consisted merely of giving chase to the animal as to a fox and tilting against him when he charged, as though he were a mounted adversary or a wild boar. A similar pastime – the sporting but in this case bloodless variant of bullfighting – is practised by country gentlemen in the cattle-raising areas of Spain to this day.

At some time in the eleventh or twelfth centuries bull-fights began to be staged in an enclosure. Spain's national hero, The Cid, who died in 1099, is said to have been one of the first, if not the first, to spear a bull in front of an audience, accomplishing the feat with a single thrust of his lance; but the matter is not proven. For a long time afterwards, to appear in a public bull-fight was the prerogative of a gentleman, and many dashing Spanish cavaliers lost their lives in the bull ring. The cult spread to Italy, which at various times has had many Spanish-born rulers. One of them, Caesar Borgia, achieved quite a reputation in the bull ring. The Emperor Charles V killed a bull in the plaza of Valladolid to celebrate the birth of his son, Philip. When in 1567 Pope Pius V outspokenly condemned bull-fighting it was not out of pity for the bulls, let alone the horses, but because too many of the nobility were getting killed or maimed at the sport. Not that his fulminations did any good.

The practice of the gentry matching themselves against bulls was finally scotched by Philip V, the first Bourbon king of Spain, who secured the crown in 1713. He detested the sport so energetically, again chiefly because he deplored the wastage of good cavaliers, that at last, and with reluctance, his Spanish courtiers discontinued their ancient tradition. But, as is obvious, that was not the end of the bull-fight. When the nobility opted out, the proletariat moved in. After what appears to have been a period of rough-and-tumble, free-for-all fighting in the ring, the present rules and ritual gradually evolved. The lowly-born but courageous matador could now wallow in the adulation formerly given to the mounted knight. Professional bull-fighters were trained (indeed, were bred, for the skill came to run in families) and achieved national fame. And around them revolved the shady world of gamblers, dealers, ticket touts, con-men and other dubious characters which most spectator sports seem to attract.

Why bull-fighting should have developed into the national sport of Spain and not

(Right) *Bull-jumpers. Cretan acrobats depicted on a fresco in the palace of Knossos, Crete, about 1550 B.C. (The author suggests that the bull depicted is tethered.)*

of other countries is a puzzle admitting of a number of half-convincing explanations. The bull-fight needs the sun, the heat and the flies, say some addicts, but Spain has no more of those amenities than have most other Mediterranean countries. Obviously the Spanish character has much to do with the phenomenon, but that statement merely invites speculation about the Spanish character. The Spanish population is no less and no more mixed than that of most other European countries, yet even neighbouring Portugal, with no natural frontiers to hedge it off from Spain, has an entirely different attitude towards bull-fights. One feels that there is a spiritual link between the bull-fight and the spectacular *autos-de-fe* which ceremonially eliminated heretics and infidels in the Middle Ages.

In earlier times bull-running and the accompanying sports were common to most European countries. In England it survived at Stamford until well into the eighteenth century. John Brand thus describes it in his *Observations on Popular Antiquities*, quoting a Stamford document of 1717:

> It is performed six weeks before Christmas. The Butchers of the Town at their own charge against the time provide the wildest bull they can get. This bull overnight is had into some Stable or Barn belonging to the Alderman. The next morning proclamation is made by the common Bellman of the Town . . . that each one shut up the Shop-doors and Gates . . .

There follow instructions for the safeguarding of strangers and travellers passing through the town, for whose protection a guard was appointed. It was also decreed that none of the citizens who expected to join in the chase was to have any iron on his club or staff. The account then continues:

> Which proclamation made, and the gates all shut up, the Bull is turned out of the Alderman's House, and then hivie, skivy, rag and tag, men, women and children of all sorts and sizes, with all the dogs in the town promiscuously running after him with their Bull-Clubs spattering dirt in each other's faces . . .
>
> A ragged Troop of Boys and Girls
> Do pellow him with Stones;
> With Clubs, with Whips, and many raps,
> They part his skin from Bones.

(Left above) *Bull-fighting; a general mêlée, the bull being attacked by a crowd with lances and other weapons. An etching by Goya.*

(Left below) *A bull-fighting etching entitled "Martincho's Daring", by Goya, 1820.*

The writer records his sense of shame at having seen "senators" and their ladies joining in the chase.

He provides the popular explanation of the event. In the time of King John, according to this story, Earl Warren, the lord of the manor of Stamford, was called out one day by the sound of a tumult among the townspeople, and found that it was occasioned by a couple of bulls fighting each other in the town meadow. A butcher set his dog on one of the bulls, which belonged to him, and the animal fled into the town. Everybody chased it, and there was tremendous commotion and havoc. Earl Warren came down on horseback and nearly fell off with laughing. While still in a good humour he gave the meadow where the fight had started to the butchers of the town, as common land for grazing between April and October, on condition that on the anniversary of the fight they should "from time to time yearly for ever find a mad Bull for the continuance of that sport".

It could be true, but, on the other hand, it could be one of those mediaeval traditions which holds more than meets the eye. Grazing rights on common land from April to October were a frequent arrangement until the time of the Enclosure Acts (eighteenth and early nineteenth centuries) and some examples still survive. But we may be sure that if the bull-running were linked with any public rights, that would be a good reason for maintaining the custom.

Brand mentions that a similar custom prevailed at Tutbury in Staffordshire at one time. There the inhabitants of the town were entitled to keep (and presumably eat) the bull, which had to be given by the Prior of Tutbury, provided they could catch it before it crossed the river.

Bull-baiting lasted even longer, being finally prohibited in England by law in 1835. It had been practised from time immemorial. William FitzStephen, who died in about 1190, wrote that, in and around London, bulls and bears were baited "every holiday before dinner". In the sixteenth century the historian of London, John Stow, comments, "as for the baiting of bulls and bears, they are to this day much frequented, namely in Bear Gardens, on the Bank's side, wherein be prepared scaffolds for beholders to stand upon."

One of the best-known place-names connected with bull-baiting is the Bull Ring, in the heart of Birmingham. Local historians think that it was probably once church property belonging to St. Martin's Church – an open space in the middle of what was then a small market town. Later it was encroached on by private houses and by a row of butchers' shops, known as The Shambles. The proximity of a bull ring to butchers' shambles is natural, for bulls were habitually baited before being slaughtered. A Birmingham writer of 1781, William Hutton, records that about a hundred and fifty

66

years earlier a citizen named John Cooper had acquired from the Lord of the Manor certain privileges, one of which was "that he should, whenever he pleased, bait a bull in the Bull Ring . . ." *The Victoria County History of Warwickshire* states,

> There are men still living who remember the time when in Birmingham and elsewhere in the county, one of the leading features of the annual wake (which usually fell on the festival of the patron saint of the parish church) was the exhibition at the Bull Ring.

In fact, the last bull to be baited in Birmingham Bull Ring suffered the ordeal in 1820. In Shropshire, and doubtless elsewhere, it continued till a year or two before the prohibiting legislation was passed. In 1833 a bull being baited at Oakengates Wake, in Shropshire, broke loose from the stake to which it was fastened and ran amok through the crowd, an escapade which caused the custom to be stopped. When, in the 1760s, John Wesley was embarking on his preaching campaigns across England, some of his opponents at Pensford, near Bristol, drove a baited bull into the congregation he was addressing in the open air. It came, reluctantly, to the very edge of the wooden table on which Wesley was standing, but "he reached down his hand and turned the shaggy, blood-stained head aside. The poor brute passed by . . ." The mob smashed the table and then were nonplussed to find Wesley still standing nearby, quietly finishing his sermon! "They slunk away a little distance, then sat down to listen."

In Cornwall the last recorded bull-baiting occurred in 1811, at Penzance. In Wiltshire a Bull Ring on Castle Hill, Mere, was used until the early years of the eighteenth century. Towards the end of the century a character Betty Dolby, who was nicknamed "Bull-riding Betty" was still remembered. Her role was to ride the bulls into the ring. At Cricklade, also in Wiltshire, bull-baiting is recorded as one of the traditional attractions at a Lammas Fair, held on the first Sunday after August 12. Enid Porter has collected accounts of bull-baiting around Cambridge in her *Cambridgeshire Customs and Folklore*. She says that Hock-tide (the week after Easter week) was the most popular season for the sport and that many of the Cambridge students joined in. The bulls were supplied by "savages called bull-haukers" and were, at least in some instances, apparently trained for the sport, which suggests that they probably lived to fight another day. The dogs were expected to seize the bull by the muzzle and never to let go. This was known as "spinning".

The English bulldog was, of course, bred primarily for bull-baiting, though since the sport was abolished fanciers have tended to exaggerate certain characteristics, particularly the bandy legs and prognathous lower jaw. The points valued by breeders when the bulldog was a "working" dog were very strong neck and jaws, a

Bull baiting, 1820; by Henry Alken.

snub nose tilted back so that he could breathe while gripping the bull, and a low under-carriage, so that the bull couldn't get its horns underneath and gore its stomach. Once the bulldog got a sufficient grip to be lifted off his feet, his own weight locked his jaws, making it impossible for him to let go.

In bull-baiting, the bull was tethered to a stake in the middle of the ring and given about fifteen or twenty yards of rope, attached to a collar. When he had been prodded to a fury by goads and other means the dogs were set loose on him. They were trained to attack him from the front, it being considered cowardly to do so from the rear, but they approached warily, their eyes fixed on the bull's nose. The contest was, in a way, not uneven, for the dogs often suffered as badly as the bull. No mercy

68

The dogs often suffered as badly as the bull.

was shown them by their owners. A dog tossed into the air would often be caught before he landed and be thrown back into the fray. Injuries were expected and disregarded. The whole procedure was, of course, accompanied by a great hulla-baloo from the excited spectators, and much money changed hands in wagers. When a bull sank to its knees exhausted, young dogs were set on it, to tear at it and so get the taste of blood. But, as noted above, some bulls at least were evidently reprieved to fight again.

There seem to have been objectors to these bloodthirsty proceedings at quite early dates. Enid Porter notes that an order of James I in 1604 prohibited the setting up of a bull ring within five miles of Cambridge. And in 1620, when a great sports day (given

Bull baiting, 1820. The bull breaks loose, by Henry Alken.

the grandiose title of "The Olympic Games"), at which the climax was to be the baiting of a "famous bull", was advertised to take place on the Gogmagog Hills south of Cambridge, a local diarist noted that he met the Vice-Chancellor of the University "on his way, as many supposed, to hinder these vain and needless proceedings". In all probability, though, the concern of the authorities was about the disorders resulting from assemblies of the more violent elements of the community rather than any compassion for the bulls.

Apologists for the vicious sport used to maintain that it was necessary to bait a bull in order that his flesh be made edible. It is perhaps possible to detect a certain logic in this contention. Maddened by pain, the bull would go berserk with rage. His blood, fortified by adrenalin, would pump vigorously through his veins and arteries. But would that make his flesh more tender and edible? No, probably the reverse. A modern technique directs a strong electric charge through beef carcases in order to *relax* the taut muscles.

70

Possibly there was involved, at least in the early days, a memory of the ancient religious belief that the blood of a sacrificial bull, spilled on the ground, would promote the growth of vegetation. This, as we have seen, was one of the fundamental beliefs of Mithraism and of the cult of Attis and Cybele, and, of course, it is founded to some extent on accurate observation, for blood *is* a good fertilizer. But beyond doubt the chief element in the popularity of bull-baiting was the gratification of the unworthy trait of cruelty in human nature.

*   *   *

To return to the still thriving sport of bull-fighting in Spain, we can see how it could have developed from other forms of sport with bulls. The following are a few basic facts.

There are approximately 450 bull rings in Spain.

In them over 1,000 bull-fights are staged annually.

About 4,500 bulls are killed.

The bull-fighting season is from March to October.

More than 200 ranches in Spain exist exclusively for the breeding of bulls for the ring.

The cult of bull-fights has spread to Spanish America, where it is popular in Mexico, Venezuela, Peru, Colombia, Ecuador, and Bolivia.

Mexico has more than 80 bull-rings and over 100 ranches breeding fighting bulls.

Bull-fights, though in most instances without the death of the bull as a climax, are also held in Portugal and southern France.

The bull-fighting season in Spanish America is more extensive than in Spain, with fights being staged in some countries throughout the year.

As might be expected, with 350 or so bull-rings in the entire country, most Spanish towns stage bull-fights. Sunday is the most popular days for these events, and few public holidays, notably Palm Sunday, Easter, Whitsun and sundry saints' days, pass without a programme of *corridas*, as they are termed in Spanish. In recent years the number of fights in the summer months in holiday resorts has increased, in order to catch the tourist trade. The Spanish word *feria*, applied to a programme of *corridas* extending over several days, is a reminder that the occasion for the fights was, originally, a country fair. Among the major *corridas* in Spain are those at Valencia in mid-March; at Toledo on Palm Sunday; at numerous centres on Easter Day; at Seville in mid-April; at Madrid for two weeks from April 15; at Cordova towards the end of May; at Barcelona at Whitsun; at Toledo and Granada (as well as at other places) on the Feast of Corpus Christi; at Bilbao for three days from June 19; at Valencia for a week from July 25; at San Sebastian, Corunna, Santander and several other northern cities in August; at Salamanca, Cuenca, Murcia, Valladolid and numerous places in September; and at Saragossa in the third week of October. But these are only some of the larger and more extensive ones. And many of the new holiday resorts, such as Benidorm and Fuengirola, are now putting on their own *corridas*. The bull-running at Pamplona, incidentally, is a five-day event beginning on July 7.

Up to five or six bulls are killed in each *corrida*, each fight lasting about 15 minutes. The fight is thus not a long-drawn-out torment for the bull. Nor is there any real doubt about its outcome. The bull has come into the ring not to engage in an even contest for his life but simply to die. The killing is ritual and conforms to a rigid pattern. Each minute act performed in the arena has meaning for the *aficionados*, as bull-fighting addicts are termed, and skilled practitioners are cheered or jeered, as in every spectator sport, according to the mastery they display of the rules of the game.

Watching bull-fighting is an emotional experience. The spectators are carried away by their feelings, as in a religious revival meeting. It is said that spectators of the games in Roman arenas were sometimes driven to such ecstasy that they experienced orgasms. While bull-fighting does not promote quite such emotional excess in the audience, the experience must be somewhat akin. Any attempt to set down in sober black-and-white what happens in a bull-ring is therefore bound to be unsatisfactory for any readers who are whole-hearted converts to the sport.

For those who are not, however, the basic programme is as follows.

The President, a citizen of some distinction, with a retired professional bullfighter at his elbow to advise him, takes his place in the official box. At a signal from him, a trumpet sounds, a brass band strikes up, and the *toreros* (the actors in the pageant) parade. Two riders in black, sixteenth-century costumes lead the procession and take their stand beneath the President's box. The President tosses them the key to the enclosure where the bulls are waiting; one of them catches it in his plumed hat, and they gallop off with it.

At the head of the procession that follows on foot is the senior matador, in conventional tight-fitting breeches, decorated with black, silver and gold embroidery. Following him in single file are several *banderilleros* and at least one picador.

Banderillas working on a bull; one of the "Tauromaquia" series of etchings by Goya.

Behind them come a motley array of reserve picadors, muleteers, grooms, carpenters and other subsidiary characters in the drama. Arriving below the President's box, every man bows to the presiding official, each with his hand pressing on the crown of his hat. They then quickly disperse to their allotted positions.

Again the bugle sounds, the door of the pen swings open, and the first bull enters the ring. He is usually bewildered by the noise and the unfamiliar surroundings, and his first reaction is to look for a way of escape. He walks, trots or rushes around the ring, according to his temperament. Suddenly he sees movement and a garment waving. It is one of the matador's assistants, flaunting a cloak. The bull, who is from long generations of animals bred for their fighting spirit, reacts instinctively. Lowering his head, he charges. In the nick of time, the *peon* with the cloak dodges behind the barrier. The bull, at a loss, pulls up sharply, then catches sight of another cloak waving on the far side of the ring. Thus he charges backward and forward, becoming

73

more and more furious with frustration. It has been part of his training for this climax of his career that he has never before been allowed to see a man carrying a cloak, so it is natural for him to be confused and to attack the cloak rather than the man.

After the *peones* have played with the bull for a few minutes, the matador takes the ring. Standing sideways to the charging bull, he allows it to pass close to him as it charges the cape which sways out from his hips like a flamenco dancer's skirt. The bull pulls up sharply, swings around, and there are the two antagonists standing side by side in the middle of the ring. The bull makes short tentative charges, the matador foils him with his cape, and so they perform a kind of grim ballet. The first act comes to an end when the bugle blows again, the matador retires, as the *picador* enters the ring.

The *picador* is the man who wields the *pica*, a kind of pike mounted on a wooden haft 8 feet long. His role is to plant the *pica* in the huge, humped shoulders of the bull. He is mounted on an aged, lean and dispirited horse, destined to be a sacrifice.

In theory the bull is guided by the matador to face the *picador*. Raising his head from his tormentor, who has puzzled him by his evasive tactics, the animal suddenly sees another enemy who may be more vulnerable. Lowering his head again, he hurtles forward and cannons into the horse and rider. According to the rules, the horse should be standing at a slight angle to the charging bull, so that when the animal strikes he hits the horse under the stomach and lifts it on his horns. This gives the *picador* the chance, if he moves quickly at the right moment, to plant his *pica* into the right spot of the bull's anatomy. He must aim not to kill the bull, but simply to weaken him and slow him down. He must not stab or try for a second hold. If he has struck truly, the harder the bull pushes the deeper the *pica* penetrates his flesh. The spectators appreciate a bull who, undeterred by the pain, will continue pushing and will return to the charge a second and third time. It is said that the bigger bulls of past centuries would take four *picas*, but three is now about the limit and some will endure no more than two or even one.

Through the intervention of English-born Queen Ena, wife of King Alfonso XIII, the horse is now protected by a quilted mattress or *peto*, which should cover its chest, stomach and right flank. The purpose is humane, but the practice hardly works out that way. Without protection, the horse was almost inevitably killed. Now it often finishes up badly wounded but still capable of another appearance in the ring. This is to the advantage of the contractors who supply horses for the rings at so much per *corrida*. If one horse can be made to perform several times it obviously saves money. So the wretched horses, understandably reluctant and terrified after one experience with a bull, are forced to undergo the ordeal time and again. Nor is the behaviour of

The picador; bull-fighting in Portugal. Note the padded horns.

the *picador* always conducive to humaneness. If the bull, frustrated at being unable to find a vulnerable spot in his adversary, is showing reluctance to charge, the *picador* will sometimes turn his horse away, deliberately inviting the bull to gore its flanks, so that he may plant his *pica* more dexterously.

The *picador* himself may well be unhorsed by the clash. Then it is the duty of the matador to step in and, with skilful cape-play, divert the attention of the bull so that the man may be rescued.

The *picador* retires. It is time for the placing of the *banderillas*. These are darts about a yard long with steel points like a harpoon. They are thrust in pairs into the bull's shoulders so that they hang down, arrow-shaped. Sometimes the matador himself places them; sometimes the job is done by *banderilleros*; it is a matter of personal

Juan Belmonte, one of Spain's leading bull-fighters in the 1940s, entices the bull with his muleta.

preference on the part of the matador. The amount of punishment the bull has to take is left to the discretion of the President, but three pairs of *banderillas* are the usual quota. Their purpose is to weaken the bull still further, especially in the shoulders, where his power lies. He will then approach his doom with his head held lower than normal, giving the matador a better opportunity to strike the fatal blow.

So far the bull has been in the ring for about 10 minutes. Now the bugle sounds for the final act. The matador, ignoring the bull, walks over to the President's box and salutes the President. He formally dedicates the bull he is about to kill either to the President or to some other person or group of spectators. Favours are sometimes thrown to him.

The matador carries a sword, his cape, and a *muleta*. This last is a tapered wooden

76

stick with a sharp steel point, around which is folded a heart-shaped piece of scarlet cloth. It is used for fencing with the bull, tiring him out and guiding him into the precise position for an efficient kill. After much daring play, in which, to the delight of the crowd, the matador tempts the bull to attack him and then avoids his assault by the smallest margin, the bull is manoeuvred into the final position. Attracting the animal's attention by the *muleta*, held low to the left, the matador rises to his full height and, ideally standing between the bull's horns, plunges his sword over the horns into the bull's upper neck. The bull collapses. If necessary, he is despatched by *puntilleros*, who finish off the animal with a *puntilla*, or dagger, while the matador withdraws to the applause of the crowd . . . that is, if they consider he has fought well.

A few final tributes are paid before the next bull is admitted to the slaughter arena. Sometimes, if the slain bull has been considered brave, the crowd will demand that the carcase is dragged around the ring to receive their acclamation, before it is taken off to the butcher's yard. A lap of honour which the chief character can hardly appreciate. The successful matador also strolls around the ring, nodding to his friends and fans, who bombard him with tributes, such as cigars, hats, flowers, women's handkerchiefs and shoes, flowers and wine-skins, some of which he deigns to catch or pick up but most of which are retrieved by his men. A special tribute to a popular and successful matador is a slice of the dead bull's ear – according to somewhat the same principle as regarding a fox's brush as the trophy of a successful fox-hunt.

Even more exotic and primitive was the former custom of cooking and eating the testicles of the bull, called the *criadillas*. They were prepared like sweetbreads and were reckoned a great delicacy. Sometimes the *criadillas* of the first bull killed were cooked while the other fights were proceeding and served to important guests before the end of the event. Ernest Hemingway remarks that Primo de Rivera was so fond of extolling manly virtues that critics said that the *criadillas* he had eaten had gone to his brain.

Five or six bulls are the usual quota of a *corrida*. There are innumerable nuances and embellishments to the above bare account. Almost every move of the matador has its technical name and is executed with as much precision as the movements of a ballet. The Spanish language is extraordinarily rich in words associated with the bull-fight.

What comment can one legitimately make about a rite which probably most Anglo-Saxons find repellent? For many *aficionados* the bull-fight comes near to being a religion, and how can one criticize a man's religion? Ernest Hemingway, who became hooked on bull-fighting when collecting material for *Death in the Afternoon* in the late 1920s and early 1930s, insisted that the bull-fight was not what Anglo-Saxons would consider a sport. Far from being an equal contest between a bull and a man, it is a ritual tragedy which inevitably involves the death of the bull. The man, too, is in danger, but the bull has normally no chance of survival. It is a kind of remorseless ceremony, albeit an exciting one.

In the drama there are four main characters or group of characters. They are (a) the bull, (b) the men who take an active part in the play, comprising the matador and his assistants, (c) the spectators and (d) the horses. The play is only tolerable if one ignores the feelings of the bull and the horses and concentrates on the bravery and skill of the bull-fighters. To seek to identify oneself with either of the two animals involved is unbearable. It is probable that few Spaniards do so. Efforts to understand what the world looks like to an animal or a bird, and what it is like to be in its skin, are a comparatively new development in the science of natural history. We now feel that crocodiles should be preserved from extinction not because of their beauty or commercial value, or even their interest to us, but simply because they are crocodiles and so have a right to live. Likewise we try vicariously to enter into the feelings of Arctic geese, ducks and swans who, having made the onerous and perilous journey from the tundra to our lakes and marshes for the winter, ought, we now feel, to be met with offers of food rather than by guns. But it seems that such sentiments are relatively new in the history of man and even now are by no means dominant. Certainly they seem not to prevail in Spanish bull-rings.

And yet . . . can we be sure? I will try to turn devil's advocate.

The bulls that enter the bull-rings of Spain are mostly three or four years old. They are in the prime of life – well, perhaps not quite, for that would be four to five years. In any country where bulls are kept primarily for meat, either castrated or whole, their lives would have ended long before then.

In spring the sight of lively lambs cavorting and gambolling in emerald green meadows, among the daisies, invites us to share with them the joy of living. But before the cornfields, now green, are turning bronze for harvest they will all be dead. They spend longer inside their mothers than outside. The young bull calves who share the meadow with them will live a little longer. Say, 18 to 24 months. But about a third of their lives will be spent in the cramped quarters of fattening yards.

This is an exercise in anthropomorphism. We are trying to imagine ourselves inside the skin of a bull. Which, then, would we prefer to be – a young beef bull in England or a young fighting bull in Spain? Certainly our life would be longer in Spain, and it would be spent with others of our kind, roaming at will over extensive pastures.

78

Death comes as the end. That is inevitable for every living creature. There is no escape for any of us. Most of us are resigned to the ultimate conclusion of our lives in what we hope will be the fullness of time, but the death of a young person, in or before its prime, strikes us as tragic. In that case, every time we eat meat, poultry or fish we are participating in a tragedy. For hardly any of the creatures that find their way on to our tables reach their prime. They are slaughtered young, in order that we may have tender meat.

Since, then, death must needs come, we rightly insist that to the animals which are killed for our sakes it must come in an acceptable form. And what is that? Not long ago a commentator to a wild-life film I was watching remarked that for an African zebra disembowelling by hyenas was an acceptable form of death. Nature is not kind. But we try to be. Animals killed for us to eat have to be properly despatched at an abattoir. There they are first stunned by an electric shock and then have their throats cut, so that they bleed to death before they recover consciousness. Such is the theory, but if we visit an abattoir we may well find it as shocking as a bull-fight. There is a smell of death and of blood, and the animals in the queue know it. They want to get out, just as the bull released in the bull-ring immediately looks for a way of escape.

A Spaniard put it to me, "If you look for human analogies, an abattoir is like a concentration camp in which the inmates queue to enter the gas chamber. A bull-fight is like a hopeless battle. In either case, death is inescapable, but in the fight the bull at least dies fighting."

But what of the wounds inflicted by the *pica* and the *banderillas*? Soldiers wounded in battle have testified that at the moment of wounding they did not feel pain. Not so long ago I had a finger crushed by a heavy log falling on it. I felt nothing for half-an-hour, after which it hurt abominably for a day or two. Recently a boy who had an arm wrenched off by machinery when rescuing a comrade was interviewed on television. After seeing that his friend was safe he ran quite a distance to the nearest house to ask for help. Asked whether his terrible wound was not hurting him he said, No.

We have spoken earlier of adrenalin coursing through the arteries of a maddened bull. This is a feeling we have all experienced in moments of sudden stress. It enables us to perform feats which under ordinary circumstances would be impossible. It is an experience which comes to some men in the heat of battle. They are seized with battle fury. The Norsemen called it "going berserk". The Malays spoke of "running amok". And undoubtedly that is what happens to the bull. Bred to fight, his boiling-point is never very high. His instinctive reaction to the unfamiliar surroundings of the bull-ring is to charge anything that moves. But his frustration at being unable to get at his tormentors drives him to a frenzy. A berserk Viking could take terrible wounds without feeling them. It is fair to assume that the same applies to the bull. His encounter with the matador lasts only a quarter of an hour. Before his wounds start to hurt, he is dead.

From the bull's point of view, perhaps the most telling criticism of the bull-fight is that he is given no chance to learn. Every precaution is taken to ensure that he has no idea about what is to happen to him. Few bulls who have entered the ring have come out alive, but those which do have learnt a lot. Of prime importance is that they have learned to ignore the lures, the waving capes and cloaks, and to concentrate on the man behind them. This makes them extremely dangerous. A bull which had been trained for a bull-fight as thoroughly as the matador had would probably be more than a match for his opponent. But, as Hemingway says, "this is not an equal contest or an attempt at an equal contest between a bull and a man". It is simply ritual killing.

Nevertheless, for most of us the merit of the abattoir as a method of killing bulls is that it is out of sight. It does not provide a spectacle to be watched, and enjoyed. But here we are moving away from a criticism of what goes on to a criticism of the spectators.

Let us look at the other animal involved in the bull-fight – the horse.

Again we will try to look at the event from the horse's point of view. What we find is intolerable. Here is an animal which has spent its life obeying and serving men. Either willingly or through hard experience it has learned to obey the bit or the human voice. Now its service is nearing an end.

This is not the case of a vigorous young warrior meeting death in battle. Rather, the parallel is of a tired old workman, whose limbs are stiff and whose faculties are failing and who is nearly ready to lie down and die.

Taken from his familiar surroundings and the people he knows (and it is said that many of the horses that die in Spanish bull-rings are shipped in from America), he is herded hither and thither, half-starved and, in many instances, callously treated by contractors who are determined to get their money's worth, and more, out of him. He is mounted by a rider whom he does not know and required to enter an enclosure filled with the reek of death. Obeying, according to the habits of a lifetime, his rider's rein, he finds himself facing a charging bull. Instead of protecting him, his rider

(Right above) *Bronze of a youthful acrobat bull-leaping. Minoan Crete about 1600* B.C. (Right below) *Pole vaulting. Juanito Apinani displays his agility and daring in the bull ring at Madrid. An etching by Goya, 1820.*

80

FUENTELAPENA 480 Kg

forces him to turn aside so as to expose his flank to the raging bull's horns. He is tossed aside, falls to the ground and is gored. But, even then, instead of being allowed to lie there to die he is, as often as not, dragged back behind the scenes, has any guts that may have escaped pushed back into the stomach cavity and is crudely sewn up, ready to face the same ordeal again later in the day or tomorrow.

Hemingway's explanation of the role of the horse seems to me to make the obscene events worse. He seeks to equate the old horse with the clown in the drama – a comic figure. They are, he says, so unlike horses that you cannot help laughing at them.

> They are like birds, [Hemingway writes] any of the awkward birds such as the adjutants or the wide-billed storks, and when, lifted by the thrust of the bull's neck and shoulder muscles their legs hang, big hoofs dangling, neck drooping, the worn-out body lifted on the horn, they are not comic; but I swear they are not tragic . . .

But that is like laughing at your grandmother because, with her false teeth spilled and her legs sprawled at awkward angles, she looks somewhat ridiculous lying there in the road after having been knocked down by a car. Thus our uncouth ancestors found something comic and interesting in the sight of a feeble-minded old woman being ducked, as a witch, in the village pond.

Still, one cannot but agree with Hemingway when he adds that "the tragic climax of the horse's career has occurred off-stage at an earlier time; when he was bought by the horse contractor for use in the ring". No one who is involved in the chain of commercial transactions which end with the appearance of the horse in the bull-ring should sleep with an easy conscience.

We can imagine that a bull, being given the choice of death in the abattoir and death in a bull-ring, might prefer the bull-ring. In no circumstances can we imagine the bull-ring being the choice of a horse. If a bull-fight cannot be staged without these scarecrows of horses, that is a very good argument for banning it entirely.

We turn to the matador.

He is the central figure in the drama and the one which *aficionados* really come to see. If one forgets about the horses, ignores the feelings of the bulls, it is possible to admire and applaud the skill and bravery of this man. Indeed, it is almost impossible not to. For about his bravery there can be no doubt.

(Left) *Bull-fighting at Cartagena, Colombia, South America. The red-and-white ribbon on the bull's back indicates the ranch which bred it.*

Tourists can buy posters advertising bull-fights which also include a space in which the purchaser's name can be inserted, testifying that John Smith, or whatever his name is, has appeared in the ring and slain so many bulls. A piece of childish gimmickry that means nothing. But imagine what it must be like to step into the ring to face a furious bull.

The bull is a big animal. It looks even bigger when seen from the level floor of the ring rather than from the raised seats in the stands. It has formidable, forward-curving horns, powered by bulging and enormously strong shoulder muscles. There are three-quarters of a ton of weight behind them. The bull is lowering his head and tossing it menacingly. It rolls its eyes, showing the whites, which are bloodshot. It is in a savage temper and obviously has it in mind to kill this man it sees in front of it. To add to the sense of impending doom, it is coloured black, with streaks of red where the blood is flowing down.

To confront such an animal; to play with him; to take liberties with him; to control him to such an extent that at the end of the ceremony he is in the perfect position for the *coup de grâce*; that is skill and courage which can be applauded.

Nor is the danger illusory. One false move can land the matador in hospital. Attached to the bull-ring is an infirmary staffed, in most instances, by doctors who have specialized in repairs to fighters injured in the ring. There is also a chapel.

Eye-witnesses have described how they have seen a matador lifted high in the air by a bull whose horn has penetrated a man's chest. The man has spun around on the horn, has been tossed and transfixed again. They have seen matadors stagger to their feet, after such an encounter, holding their hands to holes in their chests or stomachs too big for even a skilled surgeon to mend. The situation of the chapel next door to the infirmary is a convenient arrangement.

Such are the risks that the bullfighter accepts. While death is certain for the bull, it may well come to the man as well. The sight of a brave man willingly facing death can be an enthralling spectacle. There will always be plenty of people prepared to pay good money to see it, as is illustrated by the vast numbers who subscribe to see dare-devil stunt-men, such as Evel Knievel and the men who walk tight-ropes over Niagara, perform their death-defying acts.

Which brings us to the spectators.

It is probably incorrect to claim, as some have, that but for the encouragement provided by the tourist trade bull-fighting would have died a natural death. Spanish bull-fights have a devoted home audience for which they cater. It is only recently that they have taken any notice of tourists. Indeed, one of the complaints frequently made by tourists in all but the bigger towns and recognized holiday resorts has been about the difficulty of learning when and where a bull-fight was to be staged. The news was apparently circulated chiefly by word of mouth, which was of little use to holiday-makers who knew little or no Spanish. There has never been any lack of Spaniards prepared to attend the bull-fight.

Is there something in the Spanish character which makes the Spaniard sympathetic towards this spectacle? It would seem so. While sport with bulls has been abolished or has survived in only a watered-down form (as in France and Portugal) in most other countries, it continues to flourish not only in Spain but in Spanish America. The first bull-fight was held in Mexico (obviously with imported bulls, for none was indigenous to the North American continent) as early as 1529, only eight years after the Spanish conquest and only 37 years after Columbus's first voyage. A full programme of fights in Peru, Venezuela, Mexico and elsewhere in South and Central America permits Spanish matadors to earn money there on tour during the Spanish off-season, much as English cricketers play in South Africa and Australia during the English winter. And probably the biggest bull-ring in the world is the Plaza Mexico, in Mexico City, with seats for 50,000 spectators.

It has been explained to me that in the inherent fatalism, which is a part of the Spanish heritage, is a realization that suffering and death are an inevitable corollary of life. There is no escape from tragedy. The only way to make it tolerable is to dramatize it. In the fate of either the matador, the bull or the horse, the Spaniard sees a mirror of his own destiny. It is possible to feel sorrow for a bull at the very moment that one is plunging a sword into its heart. And that, of course, is what Mithra felt, too.

As one who has been a farmer for much of his life, I can appreciate that. Almost every animal I have ever reared has been destined, sooner or later, for the butcher or the knacker. I have felt sad about the necessity of wringing the neck of a hen. And soldiers have told me that, as they squeezed the trigger, they have felt regret and sympathy for the man whom they were condemning to death.

Aside from all that, however, there can be no doubt that in every nation there exists a considerable core of citizens who are not only callous about suffering but who even take delight in it. The fact that the bull-fight is socially respectable gives an outlet for their innate sadism and love of blood and death. Beyond doubt, the popularity of the Spanish bull-fight would wane rapidly if the bulls were not killed.

But the atmosphere of the bull-ring is infectious. Tourists from northern Europe to Spain and from the United States to Mexico go home and form *clubs taurinos*. Those who have caught the contagion return to the ring again and again. We are reminded of the Roman Alypius, colleague of St. Augustine of Hippo, who, from vehemently condemning gladiatorial contests, became an enthusiastic fan after he had paid one of two visits to the arena.

The Roman games degenerated rapidly after about the end of the second century A.D. Up to then there was still a certain element of fair play. The duels and affrays were brutal, bloody affairs, but, apart from condemned criminals, such as Christians were held to be, the contestants had usually a chance to come alive out of the arena. That even applied to some of the animals.

But gradually degeneration set in. The crowd demanded blood. They were no longer interested in fair play; they wanted massacre and death. The producers were hard put to devise new and ingenious forms of death to satisfy their jaded patrons.

Can a similar comment be applied to the spectators at a modern bull-fight? Not in its entirety, though recently in Portugal there has been a demand for the death of the bull, Spanish style. But the bull-fight programme has crystallized into an established ritual which varies but little. And there is a doubtful demand for a state of affairs in which the man stands an equal chance of getting killed. Nevertheless, there can be little doubt that if it were possible to revive and secure social acceptance of the Roman Games in all their bloody splendour there would be plenty of people willing and eager to pay to watch the massacres, as they do now to watch bulls being slain in a sawdust-strewn arena on a hot afternoon.

*   *   *

A few further reflections on bull-fights.

Most authorities consider that the insatiable demands for animals to fight in Roman arenas had much to do with the extinction of many species that were once common, among them the aurochs. Although the great beast survived until the sixteenth or early seventeenth centuries it had been rare for many hundreds of years. Undoubtedly, as we have seen, it contributed to the breeding of most of the domestic cattle of Europe, and it could well be that its blood runs purest in the cattle that supply bulls for the arenas of Spain, Portugal and southern France.

There are, as already mentioned, over 200 ranches in Spain devoted to breeding fighting bulls. Some of them extend over thousands of acres. Here the cows roam wild and free for most of the year, the bull being with them from April to June of each year. The calves, born in the following winter, remain with their mothers until the natural time of weaning. They would be mature at four years of age, but most are sent to the bull ring at three years.

Modern breeding of livestock is a matter of careful selection of stock. Most cattle

Semi-wild cattle on the marshes of the Camargue, at the mouth of the Rhône. Bulls are taken from the marshes to fight in the arenas at Arles, Nîmes and elsewhere in southern France.

are bred either for their milk-producing or their meat-producing potentialities. The breeding stock for producing fighting bulls are selected for their savagery and willingness to fight. But here the geneticist will detect what seems to be a flaw in the Spanish programme. The selection of stock is concentrated on the female line. It is the cows who are tested, as well as the bulls. One would have thought that, in order to produce animals of the greatest pugnacity, a bull who behaves with notable skill and bravery in the ring ought to be withdrawn and used for stud work. But this does not happen. He is sacrificed, equally with the bull who displays no courage at all.

Because of the immaturity of the bulls that nowadays are brought into the ring, they are smaller than formerly. Whether Caesar's reference to aurochs being nearly as big as elephants is an exaggeration or not we do not know, but certainly the modern fighting bulls do not approach that size. They weigh about 14 or 15 cwt and stand 4 feet or so high. This suits the art and technique of the matador very well, for

A Water Buffalo fight, held as part of the birthday celebrations of the Maharajah of Baroda, western India. The bulls are not allowed to kill each other but are urged on by backers.

he is able to rise on tiptoe and direct his mortal thrust downwards through the bull's shoulders, which he certainly could not do if the animal were towering above him. But there is always the danger that even a faltering bull will throw up his head at the critical moment and catch the matador under the arm with his horns.

Some of the best bulls are bred on the plains and marshes of Andalusia, though other ranches are distributed in many parts of the country. In southern France a race of bulls also supposed to be directly descended from the aurochs roam the marshes of the Camargue, at the mouth of the Rhône. Like the Spanish bulls, they are black and rather small. Bull-fights are held in a number of southern French towns, notably in the old Roman amphitheatres of Nîmes and Arles, in festivals towards the end of July. The bulls in these spectacles are not killed but are to assist in an act in which the climax is the snatching of a garland festooned around the animal's horns.

The Camargue cattle, which are all in one herd and privately owned, have the run of about 1,200 acres of salt marshes in the Rhône delta, though they are herded into a paddock at night. There are some 150 of them. A bell is strapped around the neck of a steer, who thus becomes leader of the herd, for the other animals tend to follow the sound of the bell. Surplus animals are sold for beef, but the breeding of bulls for sport is the primary function of the herd.

In addition to appearances in the arenas of Provençal towns, the Camargue bulls also feature in free-for-all bull runs, similar to that of Pamplona. A group of young bulls, sometimes only one, is separated from the rest of the herd. Cockades are fastened to the horns; the bulls are teased and exasperated, then turned loose in a village square or main street on a festival day. Athletic young men then leap into the ring and try to snatch a cockade. Money prizes are offered, and, as any number of men are allowed in the ring at any one time, several will sometimes combine in a concerted action. Both they and some of the bulls become expert at tactics. Occasionally such a group will be matched against experienced bulls (which have participated time after time), providing very exciting entertainment for the spectators.

Strangely, a very similar bull-fight is staged in southern India, by light, excitable fighting bulls of the Jellicut breed. The jellicut is, properly, an ornament of leaves or brightly coloured cloth which is fixed to the horns of a bull. Sometimes it includes a pendant of gold or silver coins hanging over the bull's forehead. The arena is a narrow corridor about 200 yards long, hemmed in by bullock carts. Having thoroughly excited the bull, men jump in and try to unfasten the jellicut. It is a dangerous sport, and sometimes men get killed. It is said that a price of 1,400 rupees, as against the normal price of 400 to 600 rupees, was once asked for a bull who had killed 14 men. Gradually the name of the ornament became attached to the bulls, and so to the breed, which are now known as Jellicuts.

In Thailand fighting bulls are matched against each other, having first been primed with beer or some other intoxicating liquor. The battles are said to be exciting but very seldom fatal. The bulls used are crossbred zebus.

In Portugal, too, the bull-fight lacks the dramatic finality of the Spanish version. The bull's horns are either padded or tipped with brass knobs, preventing the beast from doing any great damage with it. Its chief opponent is a mounted man who displays praiseworthy feats of horsemanship. He is in direct descent from the Portuguese aristocrat who fought bulls from horseback, using only a lance and disdaining even to draw a sword unless in mortal danger. As a climax to the show, six or so footmen enter the ring and, seizing the bull by its padded horns, wrestle it to a standstill. The bull is not normally killed – at least, not in the arena – but the fight in the ring takes considerably longer than that allowed for a Spanish bull-fight. Spanish *aficionados* claim that the Portuguese bull-fights are no less cruel than theirs and that, anyway, the bulls are killed behind the scenes after the show is over. The two versions are certainly different, and most visitors from northern countries find the Portuguese the more attractive.

The Portuguese bull-fights sometimes feature the *salteadores*, pole-vaulters who leap over the charging bulls. This was a feature, too, of shows in Roman arenas, as we have seen.

*   *   *

Sport with cattle has naturally become one of the features of rodeos and similar gatherings in the west of U.S.A. and Canada. Cowboys engage in steer roping, steer wrestling and bull riding. There is even a Bull-riding Championship in the United States, where rodeo contests date from 1847. There has been an annual festival, called Cheyenne Frontier Days, at Cheyenne, Wyoming, since 1897. One of the liveliest and most roistering of western events is the Calgary Stampede, first held in 1912 and annual since 1919 (see opposite page 129). There are now rodeos in Mexico and Australia as well.

In *Bull-riding* the cowboy rides a bucking bull, holding on with one hand only to a rope around the bull's middle. He has no saddle, bridle or stirrups. He must not use sharp spurs, must not touch the bull with his free hand, and must stay on for at least 8 seconds. Scores are for skill and technique, with extra marks awarded for obviously difficult bulls. The bulls used are mostly of Brahman type.

Steer-wrestling, or *Bulldogging*, originated with a Negro cowboy, Bill Pickett, in 1903, who, to save his fallen horse from being gored, jumped on a steer and wrestled with it. In the sport a mounted cowboy chases a steer and dives on its back from the back of his horse. He grasps its horns, drops to the ground and digs his heels in to stop the animal. Then he uses the horns as a lever to turn its head and throw it. For the operation the cowboy, or bulldogger, has the assistance of a partner, a "hazer", who rides alongside and tries to keep the steer travelling in a straight line. When the steer is thrown it should lie flat on the ground, with all four legs and its head in the same direction, the cowboy still holding on.

Steer-roping is different. A cowboy, mounted, lassoes a steer by the horns, fastens the rope to his saddle, and then stops his horse suddenly. This should throw the steer to the ground, and before it has recovered the cowboy dismounts and ties three of its legs. The winner is the contestant who finishes in the shortest time.

The background to the rodeos of the West of the North American continent is the great ranching industry which developed in the second half of the nineteenth century. As described on pages 24–5, grass grew luxuriantly on the great plains when the buffalo (bison), which had grazed them from time immemorial, were rounded up and exterminated, and cattle were moved in to utilize the rich herbage. A prime authority on the West in those pioneering days is Walter Baron von Richthofen, born in Silesia in 1848, who emigrated to the United States with his English bride in the 1870s, when the westward trek was at its peak, and settled in Denver, Colorado.

> In the early days [he writes], it was not necessary for the owners of herds to have the titles to any land; all they required was to find a good pasture with running water, which they simply occupied with their cattle.

Then the agricultural settlers began to move in. Any man had the right to 160 acres of land. He had to build a homestead there and occupy it for five years, at the end of which the government issued him with deeds to it. Soon all the desirable sites along the river valleys were occupied, and the cattle-rearers moved back from the encroaching tide of settlers. By the time that von Richthofen appeared on the scene settled agricultural land was changing hands at from 10 to 30 dollars an acre, while grazing land fetched from 2 to 4 dollars an acre.

Every cattle-owner had to register his own brand, which would be initials, figures or symbols. Some brands became known in time all over the continent, the "running W" of the King Ranch of Texas being the outstanding example. The "running W" is apparently a stylistic representation of the great, curved horns of a Texas Longhorn. I myself have a tie bearing the symbol.

With big herds wandering free over vast territories, it was obviously advantageous to organize communal round-ups, for branding and the exchange of stock. The major round-ups were held in spring and early summer, with minor ones in the fall. When the West was being reduced to order, each state governor appointed for each district in his state three round-up commissioners, whose duty was to see that the round-up laws were obeyed.

Districts were sub-divided into areas from which all the cattle could be rounded up in a day, which usually meant 10 or 12 square miles. Naturally the round-ups became great social occasions, the cattle-owners arriving with not only their herds and herdsmen but with their families and retainers, encumbered with waggons, tents and provisions for a feast. The first day was occupied with pitching tents, settling in and generally getting organized. The round-up proper did not begin until the second day.

Each owner brought in his own cattle, and scattered groups could soon be seen converging on the assembly yard. The bellowing of the cattle and the shouts of the herders came echoing through the dust-clouds. The perimeter fence was a living one of herdsmen, maintained intact throughout the day. As the different herds came in contact with each other, numerous fights broke out, but after an hour or two the cattle settled down.

When all were collected the cowboys began work, catching each calf with a lasso and throwing it to the ground, where it was branded. It was in the interests of owners to ensure that every calf was marked, for any that were missed were termed "mavericks" and, when caught later, were sold by public auction.

It was only natural that these round-ups, providing as they did one of the few social occasions of the year for cattlemen whose lives were otherwise isolated and lonely, should develop into something of the nature of festivals. After all, most of the traditional fairs of Europe originated in much the same way. In England, almost within living memory, some fairs were still being held within the ramparts of Iron Age hill-top earthworks which had, it is supposed, been constructed originally as cattle corrals. And what more natural, too, that the main items in the programme of entertainments should be contests in which the cowboys could exhibit the skills in which they excelled.

Incidentally, von Richthofen gives details of some of the largest herds flourishing in his time. The Harrold Brothers, operating in Texas, branded more than 15,000 calves in 1882 and had a herd of 60,000 animals. Charles Goodnight, who owned some 700,000 acres, had a herd of 40,000. The Prairie Cattle Company had organized its property into three divisions, two of them with over two million acres each, the other with a quarter of a million; it had around 139,000 head of cattle. Mr. A. H. Swan had recently sold his herd of 67,000 cattle in Wyoming to a new Scottish syndicate.

At that time by far the greater proportion of the beef produced in these new ranching territories was being shipped to Europe, particularly to England.

6

The Age of Improvement

That the bulls we see on modern farms or at agricultural shows or tethered in the meadows of cattle-breeding centres are very different from the great aurochs, the diminutive *bos longifrons* and the wild bulls that still roam the forests and marshes of some of the less developed countries of the world is not really surprising, when we consider what men have done to, for instance, dogs, horses, poultry and pigs since they began domesticating them. Whether we would regard a bulldog, a chihuahua, an Afghan hound or a Pekinese as an improvement on the wild dog doubtless depends on our personal preference, but generations of carefully selective breeding have certainly effected alterations. So it has been with cattle.

The principles governing programmes of livestock improvement were postulated by James Anderson, a Fellow of the Royal Society, in 1796, when they represented an approach to the subject that was still novel and revolutionary to most farmers. In a contribution published in that year by the Bath Society (later the Bath and West and Southern Counties Society) in its *Letters and Papers*, he wrote:

> It is found by experience, that individuals may be found among every breed of animals, which, from circumstances which have hitherto eluded our observation, and which it therefore exceeds our power either to accelerate or retard, may be met with, which are, in some lesser circumstances, different from others, though they still possess the general characteristics of the parent breed. And so strong is the propensity of nature in all cases to produce its own kind that if the individuals possessing these qualities . . . be selected and put to breed with others that possess qualities somewhat of the same sort, it is found that the descendants of these selected animals will, in general, be possessed of the distinguishing features for which they were selected . . . though among these also some individuals will be found to have less of it than others. And if these least approved individuals be banished from the selected stock; and those, both males and females, which possess the wished-for quality in the most eminent degree, be put to breed

together, the descendants of these will be still more improved. By continuing this mode of selection for a great length of time, the improvement . . . may be carried to an indefinite height. In this way may be produced an improved breed; which, though agreeing in the general characteristics with the parent stock from which it was selected, may possess some peculiar qualities in a much higher degree than it does.

Making due allowance for the verbosity typical of learned men of that period, that puts the matter pretty accurately. The creation or improvement of a new breed involves (a) deciding on the characteristics which one wishes to accentuate, (b) selecting individuals which have those characteristics, (c) breeding from them, and (d) continuing the process of selection from each batch of progeny consistently for generation after generation, ruthlessly eliminating animals which do not conform to the chosen pattern. In such a programme the male obviously plays the dominant part. While there is a limit to the number of progeny that a female can have, there is virtually none to that of the male. The old farming proverb, "The bull is half the herd" errs, if at all, on the conservative side. A bull can make or ruin a herd.

Interest in the improvement of cattle by these methods seems to have begun in the middle years of the eighteenth century, notably in the midlands of England. The breeder whose career attracted most publicity and who is generally regarded as the pioneer of the technique was Robert Bakewell. Born in or about 1725, he farmed at Dishley Grange, near Loughborough, in Leicestershire, where he had the good fortune to be visited in 1770 or thereabouts by one of the ablest and most energetic of a new school of agricultural publicists, Arthur Young, who in 1793 became secretary to the recently-formed Board of Agriculture. Young was so impressed by Bakewell's methods that he gave him credit for having invented them, though research in more recent times has demonstrated that Bakewell borrowed many of his ideas from other breeders in the same district, who were conducting experiments on the proper lines when Bakewell was only a youth.

However, regardless of where exactly the credit lies, it seems fairly certain that little was done about the scientific improvement of cattle and the creation of our modern breeds until well into the eighteenth century. The times were then favourable. The religious conflicts of the previous century were fading memories; the challenge of the Stuarts to the reigning Hanoverian monarchs was receding; the intentions and energies of Englishmen were being directed towards the arts of peace; and the seeds of the industrial revolution were beginning to grow at a prodigious rate. The spirit of scientific enquiry, fostered by the Royal Society (founded in the reign of Charles II), was finding practical expression in the invention of new machinery and

Robert Bakewell, pioneer of modern scientific principles of cattle-breeding, 1725–1795.

equipment, for use in such mundane activities as farming and navigation. It was an age of widespread progress.

To appreciate what Bakewell and his contemporaries did we need to know something of the material they had to work with. It could hardly have been more diverse. Every region, every district, every group of villages, had its own type of cattle. Some, apparently, were quite good, even by our standards; others were abysmally poor.

It was not that no previous attempts had been made to improve them. Good farmers must always have appreciated fine livestock and desired to possess it. But up to this time any experiments they made seem to have lacked consistency. One imagines that a farmer, visiting an acquaintance in the next county, would remark, "That's a fine bull", and would negotiate to buy him. When the time came to replace this sire the farmer would purchase another which happened to catch his fancy. There was no sustained breeding policy.

It would, indeed, have been difficult to formulate one. Success in breeding lies in not trying for too many things at once. A breeder aiming at several targets is unlikely to hit any of them squarely. And, until the Age of Improvement, cattle were regarded as triple-purpose. They were kept for meat, for milk and for draught purposes. Often the same animal had to fulfil all three functions. A cow on a peasant's holding would produce a calf a year and hence a modicum of milk, would be required to pull a plough, and would, in her old age, be slaughtered for what little meat she carried.

Scottish cattle at the beginning of the eighteenth century were even smaller than the English ones. They grazed on the unenclosed moorland by day but at nights were penned in yards. In autumn many were sold south to England, for fattening, and many of the others had to be slaughtered, in a Martinmas holocaust, for little hay was made, and turnips had not yet been introduced. Winter rations were often no more than straw or boiled chaff, and when spring at last came some of them had to be half-carried out to pasture; hence the annual ritual was known as "The Lifting".

While English agriculture and stock husbandry were admittedly further advanced at that date, the state of affairs thus described must have been widespread throughout the whole island in earlier centuries.

Yet there is some contradictory evidence concerning the progress that had been made up to Bakewell's time. Certain districts which had specialized in milk production were achieving results comparable to those of modern dairy herds. Touring Ireland in 1780 Arthur Young reported that cows in a crossbred Longhorn/Shorthorn herd he inspected at Mallow, in county Cork, were yielding up to 12 gallons each day. In Northumberland in 1771 he records an instance of a cow, belonging to a Mr. Whittam of Rothbury, which was giving the remarkable yield of 24 gallons a day. The Devon breed is now regarded as a purely beef one, but Young came across a Devon cow in Dorset which was giving $6\frac{1}{4}$ gallons a day. Similar milk yields were obtainable from herds of Suffolk Duns, reputedly good milkers, of Ayrshire cattle, of cattle in a milk-producing district of Fifeshire and of certain Shorthorn herds in Yorkshire and Derbyshire. Robert Trow-Smith considers that

94

500 gallons a year is a fair estimate of the milk production of a well-managed Wiltshire herd at this period. Even the rugged moorland Galloway was claimed by Colonel Fullarton, writing in 1793, to yield "great quantities of milk". Some of these figures, however, refer to decades when the work of the improvers could have begun to take effect, though it is only fair to add that the early breeders aimed at meat rather than milk production.

The legacy of cattle which the improvers inherited contained elements from the herds imported by every successive invader of Britain's shores. It is now thought that the original stock may have been domesticated types of the indigenous aurochs, which neolithic men found grazing on the upland pastures and sheltering in the woods which covered most of the country. It seems that through long centuries of domestication and semi-domestication two types were evolved, one much smaller than the other; and a suggestion has been made that this would be the natural consequence of a policy of killing the fattest and biggest animals and allowing the smaller and slower-maturing ones to breed. In short, it would be a reversal of the principle of intelligent selection! Certainly archaeological evidence shows that the neolithic farmers of southern England ate large quantities of beef.

Bos longifrons does not occur at archaeological sites in Britain until the Early Bronze Age, when it was apparently introduced by invaders from central Europe. For many hundreds of years cattle of both types were domesticated on British farms and probably interbred. Experts claim to detect in their skeletons similarities to several modern breeds, including the Shorthorn, Longhorn, Ayrshire, Jersey, Galloway and Aberdeen-Angus, and at one excavated site (All Cannings in Wiltshire) the skull of a polled animal has been found.

The Roman contribution to our cattle population is not known. As has been discussed earlier, it has been suggested by some (and contested by others) that the white cattle of Chillingham, Chartley and other feral herds are descended from stock imported in Roman times, but there is no certainty. Similarly, there are traditions that the Norse invaders brought with them stocks of red polled cattle, from which the polled breeds of East Anglia and Scotland have descended, but this too has been disputed. Probably there has been a desultory interchange of stock across the North Sea, the English Channel and the Irish Sea all through the centuries.

To offer an instance of the unrecorded traffic that must have occurred, when I was becoming aware of the world during my boyhood on a Wiltshire farm, in the 1920s, I learned that some of the most desirable cattle obtainable at local markets were brindled ones from the New Forest. Their milk was considered especially rich and creamy. This, I was told, was because they were the progeny of Isigny bulls on the predominantly Guernsey/Shorthorn stock of the New Forest. There had been until recently irregular importations of Isigny bulls from Normandy. These imports undoubtedly occurred, though I have never been able to find any documentary evidence for them.

Medieval records tell us little about bulls and the breeding of domestic cattle, for the reason that they deal mostly with plough oxen. One assumes that these were mostly steers, but the term may have been used to include cows used for draught purposes, and possibly bulls, too. For example, an inventory of a manor or village in Leicestershire in 1225 records that 24 peasants between them possessed 29 oxen, 28 cows and 2 heifers, but no bull is mentioned. The medieval counterpart of death duties was "heriot", a tax consisting of the best beast owned by the deceased man, hence records of heriots paid, especially at a peak period such as the Black Death, throw some light on the livestock population. The fines consist of horses, oxen, pigs, sheep and such deadstock as tools and utensils, but I find very few mentions of bulls.

When, on the other hand, we come to the demesne records, relating to the agricultural property of the lord of the manor or of some great ecclesiastical estate, bulls appear in the inventories. In 1322–3 such a farm at Wellingborough, in Northamptonshire, possessed a bull and nine cows. It seems likely that the keeping of a bull was a prerogative of the lord of the manor or chief landowner, who doubtless exacted a fee for its services. A similar custom prevailed in the Wiltshire village where I was a boy in the 1920s. Only one farmer, out of the 10 or 12 in the village, kept a bull; the others brought their cows to it and paid service fees. It was an arrangement I understood very well, for in my teens I was for a time the official custodian of the village bull.

The Black Death, already mentioned, seems to have taken its toll of cattle as well as of men – or at least they were afflicted by something similar at the same time, for a vast mortality occurred in the middle years of the fourteenth century. In *The Evolution of the English Farm* M. E. Seebohm comments that, according to some writers,

> oxen, cows and steers were not more than a third of their present average bulk. They are said to have shown a considerable reversion to type to the original Celtic shorthorn (*Bos longifrons*) and continued to deteriorate until improved by the introduction of fresh breeds from Holstein and the Low Countries late in medieval times.

By the sixteenth century considerable progress had evidently been made, for we read of Sir John Gage, of West Firle, in Sussex, who seems to have been specializing in cattle-breeding, who had 48 milking cows, 34 fattening oxen, 4 fattening barren cows, 1 fattening bull, 2 three-year-old bulls, 2 one-year-old bulls, one bulcher (which I assume is a bull calf), 24 working oxen, 4 three-year-old stores, 23 three-year-old animals (sex not specified), 14 two-year-olds, 9 heifers and 8 weaners. This was a very substantial herd, capable of comparison with a good modern one. Some other sixteenth-century herds, however, of which records survive, though of almost equal size, have no bulls.

The cattle scene in Britain on the eve of the Age of Improvement was therefore extremely complex. It would not be right to say that no improvements had been made before about 1750, for in general the cattle were decidedly better than the degenerate stock of three or four hundred years earlier. They were larger; they gave more milk and had more meat on their carcases; they were heavier and therefore more efficient for draught work. At least, some of them were, but there were tremendous variations, according to the state of local enlightenment.

As ever, the quality of the bull must have been the chief factor in improving the quality of the herd. There must have been some stock-breeders who appreciated this and who selected their herd sires wisely, and when this happened the effect was felt in all the herds in the neighbourhood, for, as we have noted, they probably all used the same bull. Indeed, perhaps they had little choice in the matter, for as late as 1811 Thomas Davis, writing a report on the agriculture of Wiltshire (a moderately prosperous and progressive county) for the Board of Agriculture, writes of a fairly recent time when cows (and sheep) were kept on common land, in a common herd. That is, from May till Martinmas (in early November) all the cows in the parish grazed the common lands under the care of a parish herdsman, being brought back to their owners for milking twice a day. We do not know whether the bull ran with the common herd, but if so the cows would automatically get served when they were ready. Under such circumstances it would be natural for the several farmers to pay service fees for the total number of cows they had in the common herd, but Davis summarizes a different arrangement which he says was popular in the dairying parts of the county. A single owner owned all the cows in the parish herd, letting them out at so much per year to the individual farmers, who thus became tantamount to share-croppers. This master cattleman bred all the replacements.

Whatever the system, much depended on the standards by which the cattle-breeder selected his stock, and particularly his bulls, although it is not certain that he always recognized this. The earliest treatise on cattle-breeding concentrate on the best type of cow to breed from and largely ignore the bull. Thus a seventeenth-century writer recommends that a good breeding cow should be "of mean stature, long body, large flank, four or five years old, of a parti-black colour or spotted black and white, her bags great, a great belly, broad between the brows, a black eye and great horns not turning in towards one another nor yet short and small but bright black, ears very hairy". Modern breeders would not disagree with many of these points but would dismiss others as quite irrelevant. Another seventeenth-century writer, Gervase Markham, who published *Cheape and Good Husbandrie* in 1631, considered that red cows were best for milk and black ones for producing the best calves. Other desirable features were said to be a crumpled horn, a thin neck, a hairy dewlap and a large udder with long, thick, white teats.

Almost every conceivable feature has been held, by some "authorities" or at some time, to be of prime importance in selecting good breeding stock. In the savannah zone, which stretches across Africa from Ethiopia to Senegal, it seems to be generally conceded among the nomadic herdsmen that the best criterion for judging cattle is the size of the horns! In consequence, some of their bullocks support (albeit with difficulty!) upcurved horns 3 or 4 feet long and broad and heavy in proportion. Ridiculous though the criterion appears at first sight to be, I can see that it may have a certain validity. Presumably big horns are matched by big bones and a heavy frame, hence considerable stamina, which is what these animals need for their long treks in search of grazing. And in recent years it has been proved that when these big-framed beasts are put into beef feedlots of the American style and fed adequate balanced rations they put on flesh faster and more economically than do European types.

There is also the point that the horns serve as useful handles, or levers. Cattle I have seen being ferried across the river Gambia have been hauled on board the boat by a crane, with a rope fastened around the base of those massive horns. Perhaps this convenience, rather than any excellence in meat production or ability to exist on a low diet, is the factor which counts with the herdsmen. But, in any case, the criterion is no more nonsensical than the one by which my father and his neighbours used to select bulls (and cows) in southern England in the 1920s and 1930s. The predominant local breed was the Shorthorn, and farmers worked on the principle that the best Shorthorn was a roan one. They selected, in fact, on colour.

What Robert Bakewell and his contemporaries did was to cut through the mass of confused lore about breeding standards. Their approach was refreshingly clear and logical. They decided on just what they wanted. Then they set about producing it by breeding and inbreeding from animals which exhibited the desired qualities. Subsidiary characteristics, such as colour of the hair, the size of horns, the length of hair in the ears and the colour of the teats, were ignored.

Bakewell himself chose to breed for beef. He wanted beasts with good, meaty

Old types of cattle, from a painting by Corbould, 1879.
Left to right; back row – *Suffolk or Norfolk; Sussex; Glamorgan;*
middle row – *Hereford; North Wales;*
front row – *Devon; South Wales cow; Shorthorn bull; Derbyshire Longhorn.*

carcases, particularly with masses of flesh on their hindquarters, and he wanted them to grow and fatten quickly. All else was subsidiary, and a criticism (largely justified) of his work was that he sacrificed many other desirable qualities and especially the propensity for milk production. Because of this his selected breed, the Longhorn, fell into disrepute and eventually came near to extinction. Nevertheless, despite these shortcomings, Bakewell indubitably deserves his reputation as the pioneer of modern livestock husbandry. Although he made mistakes, he correctly enunciated the principles of livestock breeding. He demonstrated what had to be done and how to set about it.

At this stage a brief but more detailed look at the material available to Bakewell is in order. Although at that time there were no breeds as we know them, with carefully formulated points regarding conformation, yet certain distinct and largely regional types, though with considerable local variations, had been evolved.

99

The *Longhorn*, predominant type of midland England and also found in many other parts of the kingdom, seems from its appearance to have been a direct descendant of the primeval aboriginal cattle of the forests. It had long, sickle-shaped, down-curved horns, a massive body and generally a brindled coloration. In particular, it flaunted the colour feature known to cattle-men as "finching" – a white stripe along the spine and extending to the tail. This it shares with the *Old Gloucestershire* breed, another primitive type, and with the ancestors of the Herefords. "Finching" is a natural colour feature, serving the same purpose as the warning scut of a fleeing rabbit or deer. I realized that years ago when I went to see a bunch of Old Gloucestershire heifers running free in a park at Colesbourne, in Gloucestershire. Disturbed while grazing, they made off into the autumn woods, their dark brown colour merging quickly into the background of dead bracken and bronze leaves, except for the "finching", which flashed an alarm signal to any other animals that might be around. So must the aurochs have warned its herd companions of the approach of hunters in the primeval woods.

The *Shorthorn* perhaps owed more strands of its ancestry to the Celtic *Bos longifrons*. It had also received considerable infusions from Holland, a country from which the original cattle imports were coloured red-and-white or roan, rather than the black-and-whites which later became known world-wide. In Bakewell's time the eastern counties of Yorkshire, Durham and Lincolnshire were the Shorthorn stronghold. Lincolnshire possessed large numbers of all-red Shorthorns from which the *Lincoln Reds* were soon to be developed as a separate breed.

Some of the Yorkshire Shorthorns were polled, and polled cattle predominated farther south, in East Anglia. The most numerous type was known as the *Suffolk Dun*, "dun" covering a range of colour from drab brown to greyish-yellow. Suffolk Duns were considered to be excellent milk producers, and surviving records show that some of them were capable of yielding up to 6 gallons of milk per day. Being small, they also fattened quite quickly, and drovers collected them in great numbers for driving down to the fatstock markets of London. From these Duns the *Red Poll* breed was later evolved.

South of the Thames a distinct type of deep-red cattle was concentrated in Sussex and western Kent. Their main recommendation seems to have been as a draught animal, but they were solid, heavy beasts and so in demand in the London meat markets. An improved type, modified by crossing with Channel Island cattle, was known as the *Kentish Home-bred* and had a better milk yield.

Devon also had red cattle of somewhat similar type. By the eighteenth century they were widely known throughout lowland England as good beef animals and had been introduced to many other parts of the country. Some writers of that time regarded *Sussex* and *Hereford* cattle as merely varieties of *Devons*.

Long before the eighteenth century the Channel Islands seem to have acquired a reputation as a source of good milk cattle. Frequent importations were made to the southern ports of England, from which the animals were dispersed all over the country, even penetrating into Scotland. As early as 1763 the States of Jersey passed a decree prohibiting the importation of any cattle *into* the island, the purpose being to stop French breeders from using Jersey as a staging-post for getting cattle into the lucrative English market. In England all the Channel Island cattle were known indiscriminately as *Alderneys*. They seem to have been variable in colour, but all were good milking types. The modern South Devon is almost certainly developed from crosses between the red Devon and imported Channel Island cattle.

Somerset had a type of cow which has now become extinct, the *Somerset Sheeted*. Its rear half was entirely white, as if it had a white rug or sheet thrown over it. The fore-quarters were red or yellowish-red.

In Gloucestershire and the neighbouring counties the *Old Gloucestershire* type, now extremely rare and only saved from extinction by a hair's breadth, was predominant. As already mentioned, it was a dark-brown, sometimes almost black, animal, with conspicuous finching. It owed its popularity to the quality of its milk, which, being rich in large globules of butterfat, was deemed ideal for the making of Double Gloucester cheese. At one period it seems to have been the prevailing type in the cheese-producing pastures of north Wiltshire, but by Bakewell's time it was being superseded by the Longhorn. Westwards from Gloucestershire the *Glamorgan* type of cattle, now extinct, was very similar to the Old Gloucesters, and over in Pembroke-shire the *Castle-martin* cattle also demonstrated their kinship by their bold finching.

In Herefordshire and the border counties of England and Wales cattle of Long-horn type seem to have been indigenous and to have been used for all purposes, including much draught work. However, there is some evidence that from quite early times red was the predominant colour, as in Devon. There is also a tradition that noteworthy imports of Dutch cattle were made by Lord Scudamore in the middle of the seventeenth century and had a considerable influence on the breed.

Wales had three main types of cattle – red, black and white – though with varying degrees of dilution by English breeds. The white, a few of which survive in semi-domesticated herds, seem to have made little contribution to *Welsh* commercial cattle. The red have become extinct, except insofar as they have contributed to the development of the Hereford. The blacks were extremely variable, ranging from feminine dairy types to rugged beef ones, their performance made unreliable by crossing with each other and with other breeds. In general, though, in the eighteenth century Wales was looked upon as a source of beef cattle, immense numbers of which were driven across England, by traditional drovers' roads, to London. From these nomadic hordes some of the most attractive cattle were from time to time siphoned off to form alien herds in many of the English counties. Welsh black cattle were quite well known in counties as far distant from their homeland as Kent and Norfolk.

In northern England, Shorthorns, as we have seen, made up the bulk of the cattle population of Yorkshire and other counties east of the Pennines, while on the western side, in Lancashire, Longhorns predominated. Indeed, eighteenth-century writers considered Lancashire to be the original home of the Longhorn, from which it had spread southwards into the Midlands.

Scotland had a dairy breed or type in the *Ayrshire*, which was also known as the *Dunlop*, because it was said to have originated in the parish of Dunlop in the seventeenth century. Already by the eighteenth century it seems to have resembled closely the Ayrshire of today. Its ancestry is in doubt but apparently included much Dutch and Channel Island blood on a basis probably of Longhorn with some mingling of Shorthorn. Some of the early Ayrshires had distinct finching.

In another lowland region of Scotland, the peninsula of *Fifeshire*, another dairy type had been developed. It is now extinct but seems to have been a useful dual-purpose animal, producing milk notable for its richness rather than its quantity. Its large carcase commended it as a beef type. It was black and had up-curved horns, like the modern Ayrshire.

South of the Highland Line in Scotland, and apart from the two dairying districts just mentioned, the dominant type was the *Galloway*. Then, as now, it was a rough, shaggy, hardy animal, bred on the austere moors of the province from which it takes its name. It provided vast numbers of cattle for the English markets, and when these lean, healthy animals moved south for a period of fattening on the lush English pastures they put on flesh with extraordinary rapidity and produced excellent beef. The polled type, now universal, was developed in order to prevent the cattle in the huge droves from injuring each other on their southward trek. Modern opinion is that in its ancestry it may owe a considerable debt to infusions of Longhorn blood, on a basic indigenous type. That Scottish breeders knew how to eliminate horns by a breeding programme, long before Bakewell's time, is interesting. Galloways were in general poor milkers, but milking strains had been developed in a few pockets of good dairying country.

The cattle of north-eastern Scotland, from which the modern *Aberdeen-Angus* were developed, were at this time a heterogeneous collection of small cattle, of virtually all colours and both polled and horned. They had little to commend them until an improvement in the general standard of agriculture, and notably the introduction of turnips, provided them with a better diet than heretofore.

The *Highland* type, little different from animals of the breed today though somewhat smaller, accounted for the cattle population of the Highland zone. They were so diminutive that even fat cattle ready for the butcher weighed no more than about 5 cwt. On the other hand, the meat was said to be of excellent quality, and considerable numbers went south to English markets.

In Ireland numerous importations of English types of cattle had crossed with the indigenous animals, which were mainly small and black. Small numbers did the reverse journey across the Irish Sea but were not regarded in England as of any great commercial value. Their modern counterparts are the *Kerry* and *Dexter*.

There remain the anomalous and puzzling white cattle of Britain, a fuller account of which was given on pages 28–30.

In addition to these well-known animals, however, there is now a rare domesticated breed of white cattle, the *British White*. Once widespread, it is now confined to a few herds in the Midlands and Norfolk. Where the Chillingham cattle have red ears, muzzles, eye-lashes and other points, in the British Whites these features are black; and the British Whites are polled. They are as docile as any other breed – more so than some – and in performance resemble the dual-purpose Dairy Shorthorn. They are very similar to a breed which is kept extensively in the northern parts of Sweden, but they seem to have contributed little to other British breeds.

*   *   *

Such, in brief, was the material at the disposal of Bakewell and his contemporaries. It is not really surprising that he chose the Longhorn. While he was doubtless familiar with at least some of the other types, the local one would naturally give him the widest choice of individual animals, and it was also the one on which some of his neighbours had already done much preliminary work.

About 1720 Sir Thomas Gresley, of Drakelow, near Burton-on-Trent in Staffordshire, laid the foundation of a herd of Longhorns which became known in the district for their excellence. Between 20 and 30 years later a Mr. Webster, who farmed at Canley near Coventry, about 30 miles from Drakelow, bought some of Sir Thomas's bulls to improve his own herd. Here is one of the earliest documentary references to the recognition of the importance of the bull in schemes for livestock improvement. Webster achieved a tremendous reputation throughout the Midlands for his experiments in cattle breeding, and it is not surprising that Bakewell heard of them. When he started his own programme he based it on two heifers from the Canley herd of Mr. Webster and a Longhorn bull purchased from Westmorland.

From this foundation stock Bakewell in 1770 bred an outstanding bull, "Two-penny", – one of the first bulls in all history whose name is recorded. Thereafter the breeders and their publicists concentrated on the sires. Another of Bakewell's Dishley bulls, distinguished only by the letter D, became the sire of a remarkable bull, "Shakespeare", every one of whose progeny, it is said, could be distinguished at a glance, so similar were they to their father. "Shakespeare" was the sire of the Rollright herd, the property of Robert Fowler of Little Rollright, Oxfordshire, which some contemporaries considered was even better than Bakewell's herd at Dishley.

Tremendous attention was attracted to Bakewell's experiments, especially after Arthur Young had written about them. Distinguished visitors and fellow cattle-breeders came from all over the country to inspect his flocks and herds and were entertained by Bakewell so generously that he nearly bankrupted himself and is said to have died in comparative poverty. Although his own programme of Longhorn improvement eventually foundered, the breeding principles which he employed became widely accepted and led to the establishment of the breeds we now know.

The details of his programme he never revealed. He liked his visitors to see and admire his animals, but he gave away no secrets. Perhaps his reticence was more effective than direct proselytizing methods would have been, for visitors, confronted with these admirable cattle and being given only half the story, went home and worked out the rest of it for themselves. But the outline of what he did is plain. Having decided exactly what he was aiming for, he chose animals which exhibited the desired characteristics and bred from them, using in-breeding deliberately for generation after generation and ruthlessly discarding any calves which did not conform to the type he had in mind. "Twopenny" he used to hire out to serve his neighbours' best cows at 5 guineas per service, perhaps with the stipulation of an option on any calves which he fancied. He thus achieved a wider dissemination of the qualities of this excellent bull.

The techniques he used with Longhorn cattle he had first tried out on sheep, with which he was more successful, founding the New Leicester breed, which were in many respects superior to anything previously known. His failure with the Long-horns probably resulted from a too narrow concentration on the selected characteris-tics. Before his time the Longhorns were a dual-purpose, or all-purpose, breed, but

Bakewell visualized them solely as meat-producers. He wanted a small-boned animal which would put on a lot of flesh in the right places quickly. Everything else was secondary and could be sacrificed. In particular, he discarded the milking qualities of his cattle.

Possibly he did not realize the extent to which milking qualities are transmitted by the sire. It is, after all, a hidden inheritance. While the stamp of the sire, in the matter of colour and conformation, may readily be observed in his progeny at a quite early age, his legacy of milk production propensity can only be studied when his daughters are mature enough to breed. Bull progeny testing programmes are now one of the main tools in cattle breeding, but it took a long time to get their value widely appreciated. Indeed, they have come into their own only since the development of artificial insemination. By the time that the capacity of a bull to transmit the ability to produce high milk yields has been proved, by the performance of his daughters, grand-daughters and great-grand-daughters, the bull himself may be dead. Now he can produce almost innumerable further offspring, from deep-frozen semen, long after his demise.

One reason for the failure of Bakewell's Longhorns was the success of other breeders, using his methods, with a competitive breed, the Shorthorns. In 1784 two brothers, Robert and Charles Colling, who had studied Bakewell's work, began a similar programme based on a Shorthorn bull, "Hubback". Although casually purchased, "Hubback" proved to be a winner, though he was hardly of pure Shorthorn blood, having traceable ancestry to both Dutch and Highland animals. However, he faithfully transmitted to his progeny all those features to which his owners attached most importance. And in due course from his line sprang, in 1804, an even more famous bull, "Comet", the first ever English bull to be sold for a 1,000 guineas. As an illustration of the Collings' methods, "Comet" was the son of a bull on his own daughter; his sire was the progeny of brother and sister; and the sire's dam was the daughter of a bull on his own mother.

Where Collings' Shorthorns scored over Bakewell's Longhorns was that they continued to be dual-purpose. Their undoubted meat-producing qualities were not achieved at the cost of milk production. Bakewell was rather too early in specializing. The demand was still for a milker which would have a saleable carcase when its milking days were over and which would produce calves that would appeal to the butcher if they were not needed for herd replacements. That demand has, indeed, never really declined, and even today most of Britain's home-produced beef comes from surplus animals from dairy herds.

As it happened, in the end its dual-purpose qualities proved the undoing of the

Shorthorn breed. Early in the nineteenth century the breed split into beef and dairy types. The beef animals, largely developed in Scotland, decreased in size and became beef producers *par excellence*. The dairy types were formed into a separate breed, the Dairy Shorthorn, still taking a pride in their dual-purpose status. By the end of the nineteenth century Dairy Shorthorns were dominant over the greater part of England. But problems arose from the fact that the beef and dairy breeds were not distinguishable by eye, and there was much interbreeding. Hence no farmer buying in the open market could be sure that the roan animal of splendid appearance would turn out to be a good milker or produce little milk at all. Consequently when a breed, the black-and-white Friesian, with a guarantee of heavy milk yields, became available it swept the board.

After, or contemporaneously with, the success of the Longhorn and Shorthorn breeders, farmers in other parts of the country set about replicating the exercise with their local stock. The early Hereford breeders made their first object the production of a large heavy animal which, after working on the land for about six years, would fatten satisfactorily on the rich grazing pastures of the Midlands. Devon breeders, and no doubt others as well, had the same idea in mind, and in time the beefing qualities assumed major importance while the required working life yoked to the plough grew shorter.

The Herefords were taken in hand by several farming families, notably the Tully family of Huntington, in Radnorshire, and the Gallier family, of Leominster, who laid the foundations of their development into a superb beef breed. The early stock seems to have been of many colours, many of the animals being even without the white face which later became the hallmark of the breed. Imported cattle from Holland in the mid-seventeenth century are said to have introduced the white face, but for some time it was regarded with disfavour. The story of the event which led to its general acceptance, though I doubt whether it can be authenticated, was widely disseminated, as the following account, given by J. Kersley Fowler reminiscing in Buckinghamshire late in the nineteenth century (*Records of Old Times*), suggests.

Mr. Tully's herdsman came to his master one Sunday, as he was returning from church, and told him that his favourite cow, which was daily expected to calve, that morning had produced a bull calf *with a white face*, such an event never having happened in his herd before. His master at once ordered him to slaughter the calf, as he dared not let it be known that such a stain of impure blood should be found in his well-reputed pure herd. The man begged him to go and see before deciding, as it was the finest calf he had ever seen. Mr. Tully, after seeing the animals, agreed with his man that it was a wonder, and out of curiosity he would have it reared. This was done, and

106

Robert and Charles Colling, pioneer breeders of Shorthorns; 1749–1836.

he grew up to be a remarkably fine animal. The bull was mated with his best cows, and the progeny became celebrated for their white faces.

J. Kersley Fowler, who set down this story in 1898, says that even in his day the colours of the Hereford were not rigidly established. He adds,

> Sometimes the face is mottled with red, whilst many of the best Hereford cattle I have grazed and fattened have been of a light brindled colour, and I have seen Herefords all pure white, but the latter are extremely rare.

In Devon the red cattle were taken in hand by Francis Quartly, of Molland, starting in 1791. His work, continuing well into the nineteenth century, is thus later than that of the great Midland breeders, and he operated in a rather different way. Apparently during the Napoleonic Wars Devon cattle were in such demand by breeders and fatteners in other parts of the country that supplies were becoming depleted. Quartly therefore set about buying the best of all the cattle he saw offered for sale, and, over the years, thus built up a superb Devon herd.

The steps taken by the States of Jersey to guard the purity of their cattle, by enactments in 1763 and 1789, have already been mentioned. Since then the island's cattle have been bred pure. The ban on imports was imposed much later in Guernsey and Alderney, with the result that the Guernsey breed became modified with crosses with Dutch and Spanish cattle.

Dutch imports, and probably some from the Channel Islands, played their part in the development of the Ayrshire breed, the type of which was well established in Ayrshire by the end of the eighteenth century, though little is known of the breeders responsible. The modern Aberdeen-Angus is the achievement of work begun no earlier than the 1830s, and the improvement of the other types mentioned and their establishment as recognized breeds were also late developments. The *British Friesians*, now easily the most numerous breed in Britain, had no breed society until 1909, although very large numbers had been imported (though chiefly for slaughter) over the previous three or four decades. Before that, in the middle of the nineteenth century, the traffic had been in the other direction, with big shipments of English Shorthorns being sent to Holland to reinforce the Dutch herds after ravages by disease, so there was undoubtedly much Shorthorn blood in the Friesians which came back.

It is worth remembering that the tremendous improvements effected in British cattle, and the establishment of the pure breeds we know, were the work of a comparatively few dedicated, enlightened and energetic breeders. The rank-and-file farmers carried on much as before, even as many do today. The farmers among whom I was brought up in the 1920s and 1930s knew nothing of scientific breeding methods. They bought an animal, bull or cow, because they liked the look of it. Even some of the leaders in the farming world at the time of Bakewell and in the succeeding century failed to understand what had been done. Thomas Davis, quoted above, took a good look at the improved Longhorns supplying milk for the north Wiltshire cheese-making industry in the early years of the nineteenth century and advanced carefully-prepared arguments for replacing them by Devon cattle, not realizing that what he was advocating was a return to the age-old practice of fetching attractive animals from other regions, regardless of their individual breeding and heredity.

Even the breeders themselves, despite their avowed intention of producing quick-maturing rather than massive animals, could not resist occasionally yielding to their inherent conviction that, after all, size meant excellence. It was the Colling brothers who, from their superb Shorthorn herd, bred the 'Durham Ox', a celebrated monster which, after attaining the weight of 27 hundredweight (3,024 lb.) at the age of five years, was then sold to a travelling showman with whom it travelled the country for the next six years. They also exhibited a white heifer which turned the scale at 2,300 lb. In 1801 the first Hereford prize at Smithfield Show was a gigantic beast which stood 6 feet, 7 inches at the shoulder, was 8 feet 11 inches in length, had a girth of 10 feet 4 inches, and weighed (dead) 1,976 lb. Then there was the "Airedale Heifer", a Shorthorn bred by a Mr. William Slingsby near Keighley, in Yorkshire, which weighed 2,640 lb. when killed in about 1820. "She was rising six years old when killed and cut nine inches of clear fat on the ribs". Which last is a qualification which would earn her no marks at all today.

The alleged portraits of two of these and of many more illustrious animals are in a unique collection of prints and paintings of British farm livestock housed in the library of Rothamsted Experimental Station at Harpenden, Hertfordshire. Comments on them are found in the next chapter.

In spite of errors and shortcomings, exaggerations and failures, the improvers of Britain's livestock breeds in the eighteenth and early nineteenth centuries did work of inestimable value. Once the breeds were established, breed herd books were instituted and kept with meticulous accuracy. The breeds were not only admirably suited to the purposes for which they had been designed but were utterly reliable.

In consequence, when the newer countries of the world were ready to develop their livestock industries, it was chiefly to Britain that they turned for stock. The immense cattle herds of Australia, New Zealand, South Africa, the United States of America, Canada and temperate South America are composed largely of breeds of British origin. The beef industry of South America was founded largely on Beef Shorthorns, with Aberdeen-Angus and Herefords moving in later and capturing much of the market. The ranches and beef feedlots of U.S.A. and Canada are filled with Herefords and Aberdeen-Angus. Approximately 80% of the beef cattle of New Zealand are said to be Aberdeen-Angus. Australia has almost every British breed, with big populations of Herefords, Devons and Sussex. Sussex and Devon cattle have done particularly well in the warmer countries, such as Brazil, East Africa and Central America, as have the Red Polls, among dairy breeds. Jerseys and Guernseys are everywhere. In spite of their feminine and dainty appearance, Jerseys are very hardy and thrive in such cold countries as Alaska and northern Canada. Finland,

"The Pleasure of Success". A later 19th century engraving.

among other countries, has its own Society of Ayrshire breeders. Even the shaggy Highlanders have found new homes in Russia and the Falkland Islands. Virtually every country in the world has been able to find British cattle which will acclimatize satisfactorily and produce efficiently what is required of them.

Leading breeders from all over the world return to Britain year after year to buy high-priced stock to replenish and reinforce their herds. In the southern hemisphere there tends to be a gradual deterioration of type which compels regular reinforcement by stock from the original source. The Royal Agricultural Show at the National Agricultural Centre at Stoneleigh, in Warwickshire, where the best of

British livestock is on display for four days each July, is a forum and meeting-place for cattlemen from, by the latest count, more than a hundred nations.

*   *   *

Although much of the pioneering work of modern stock-breeding was done in Britain, the nineteenth century saw similar developments in a number of European countries. Notes on the origins of some of the breeds will be found in the Appendix. In America the eastern states acquired a basic stock of cattle from Europe by the middle of the seventeenth century, but these were of the nondescript, all-purpose types then universal in Europe. Some of the improved Shorthorn breed are reported to have been sent from England to Virginia as early as 1783, but the impact of this importation was not apparently very great. After the American Civil War the Texas Longhorn type, moving up from the south, mingled with the "native" cattle pouring into the prairies from the east. Improvement of cattle stocks by the importation of pure-bred animals from Europe belongs chiefly to the second half of the nineteenth century and subsequently. It was not until the early years of the twentieth century that America began to develop its own breeds, such as the *Beefmaster, Brangus* and *Charbray*. In Australia the *Murray Greys* first appeared in 1905. In Canada the *Hays Converter* was not developed until the 1950s.

The various cattle breeds or types of Africa, India and the East have evolved more by natural selection than by judicious human selection, though zebus exported to other countries, notably South America, have played a prominent part in the development of improved stock. In very many countries the potential of the in-digenous stock is now being scientifically examined. It is often found that the local breed carries important genetic characteristics which, when matched with the improved production of imported stock, results in the breeding of some profitable and highly efficient animals.

In all countries, even in Western Europe, we are still in the middle of the Age of Improvement.

7

Were They Really Like That?

The previous chapter contains references to some of the aberrations and exaggerations thrown up by early experiments in cattle-breeding. The monstrous "Durham Ox", the prize-winning Hereford at Smithfield Show in 1801, and Mr. William Slingsby's "Airedale Heifer", are given as examples. The measurements recorded for these animals are highly impressive, and their surviving portraits even more so. In fact, some of the latter are so grotesque as to be almost unbelievable. Looking at them we are impelled to exclaim, Were they really like that?

So incredible are they that twenty years or so ago I undertook a little investigation to discover whether the artists had indeed painted what they saw. This chapter, a short digression from the main theme of the book, summarizes what I learned.

One of the best collections of animal pictures of the period is at Rothamsted, in Hertfordshire, England's premier agricultural research station. It consists of nearly a thousand prints, paintings, lithographs and engravings, covering a period 1780 to 1910, though by far the greater number of pictures belong to the first fifty years of the nineteenth century. More than 75% of them depict cattle; of the rest, about 120 are of sheep, 50 of pigs, 15 of horses, 28 of scenes, and 15 are portraits of livestock breeders. The nucleus of the collection is a large number of prints, bequeathed to Rothamsted by Francis, fourth Baron Northbrook, who was a great connoisseur of art and an authority on British livestock and who died in 1947. Rothamsted already possessed many livestock pictures of historical interest, and subsequently others have been added, making the collection probably the finest in existence. The bulk of it is

(Right above) *Park bull at Chartley, Staffordshire, where one of the herds descended from the ancient wild white cattle of Britain survives.*

(Right below) *A Highland bull. There is something primitive about their shaggy, rough appearance and their enormous "handle-bar" horns.*

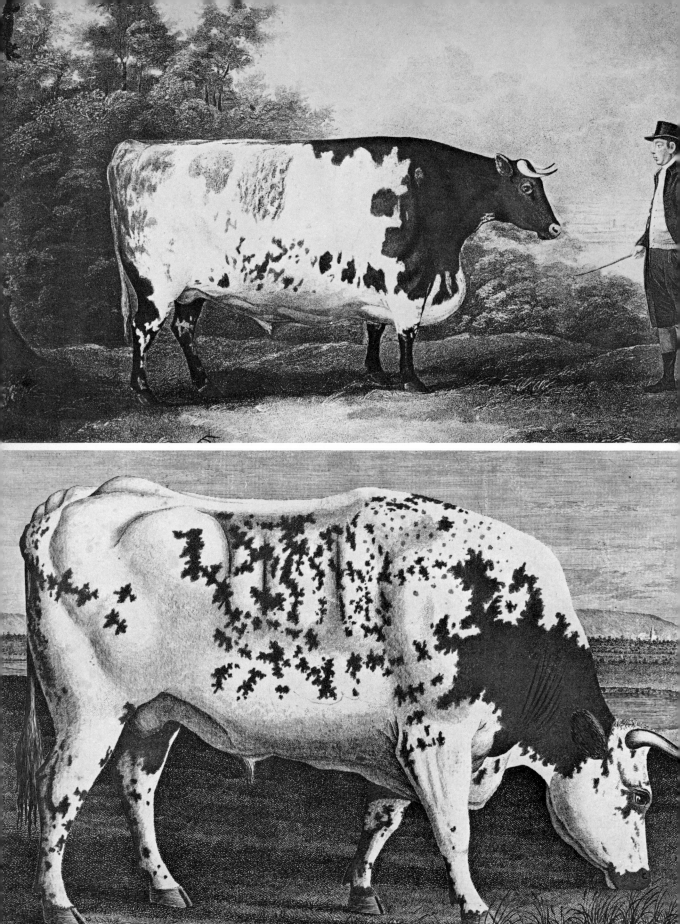

now kept in large folders in the Rothamsted library, with some selected items, framed, exhibited in the halls and offices.

The earliest cattle print at Rothamsted is a line engraving (by J. Bailey from a painting by George Cuit) of the "Blackwell Ox". Dated 1780, it is of an animal which was slaughtered, at the age of six years, in 1779. It therefore belongs to the first recognized period of cattle improvement.

Now Blackwell is a village in county Durham, the county which was the home of the old Teeswater type from which the Shorthorn breed was evolved. In 1784 Robert and Charles Colling selected a bull from this district, "Hubback", as the foundation sire of their improved Shorthorn breed (and fifty years later a noted Shorthorn breeder testified that "we have no superior shorthorns which do not claim descent from ... 'Hubback'"). In the "Blackwell Ox", therefore, we are probably looking at an example of the old domestic stock of England before the improvers got at it.

It is not a bad animal. A bit heavy on the forequarters and somewhat short in the body but, on the whole, quite well proportioned. There is none of the gross obesity so evident in the portraits of cattle of twenty and thirty years later. One also has the feeling that George Cuit drew it from life; it does look like a real animal. It is grazing, and walking as it grazes, as cattle do.

Intimations of unreality begin to creep in with the "Durham Ox", of which we have an etching (by J. Whessell, from a painting by J. Boultbee), dated 1802. This celebrated animal has already been referred to in the previous chapter. Bred by Charles Colling, it spent six years touring Britain and displaying its 27 hundred-weight of flesh and bone to fascinated audiences. At the time of the portrait it stood $5\frac{1}{2}$ feet high at the shoulder, was 11 feet long and measured just over 3 feet across the middle of the back.

The picture shows the ox in conventional posture, full side on and legs perfectly positioned. The body is roughly rectangular, though with an over-fat and pendulous dewlap. Although this animal is very different from the "Blackwell Ox", one feels that, making allowances for the manipulations of Mr. Colling, this is probably what it looked like. The breeder had evidently been working for a deep, massive body and had been so successful that the head appears small and the legs short in proportion. But not outrageously so.

(Left above) *The "Durham Ox", 1802. It weighed 3,024 lb at five years and was taken around the country on exhibition by a travelling showman.*
(Left below) *The "Blackwell Ox", of the improved Teeswater breed (later to become known as Shorthorns). Killed at Darlington in 1789, it weighed 2,278 lb and stood 5 feet $9\frac{1}{4}$ inches at the shoulder.*

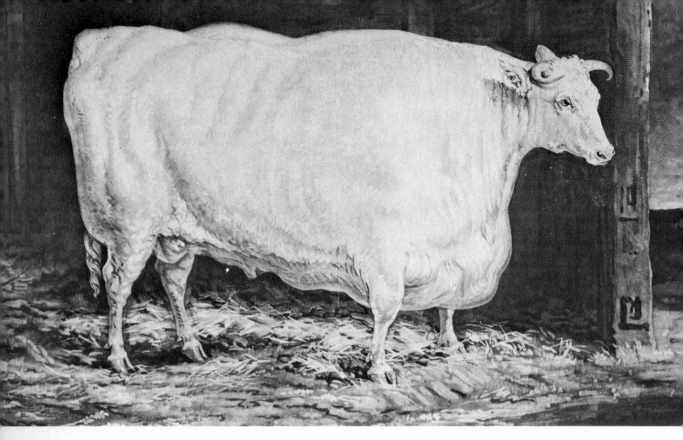

The "Durham White Ox". In 1813 at seven years old it weighed 3122 lb and stood 5 feet 4 inches at the shoulder.

It is far otherwise with the flood of cattle pictures which now began. The "Durham Ox" achieved such popularity that, according to the caption on the print, more than 2,000 orders for copies were taken in the first year. The portrait started a vogue in animal portraits, just as the ox itself helped to set a fashion in animal breeding. Whether from choice or compulsion, artists began to copy slavishly the pattern set by Boultbee and Whessell, though exaggerating it more and more grotesquely as the years passed.

It is difficult to determine just how exaggerated the obesity was. The breeders of that time were breeding for flesh and weight, and certainly some of them overdid it. No modern breeder, for instance, would have purchased the "Craven Heifer" (the engraver is J. Whessell and the painter Fryer) for breeding purposes. A Shorthorn, she is still termed a heifer at the age of four years, in 1812. She then weighed 2,468 lb. and was far too fat.

From a perusal of the Rothamsted prints, one would say that the fashion reached its climax in the "Airedale Heifer", painted by J. Bradley and engraved by R. G. Reeve in 1820. Here we see a vast, slab-sided creature, as rectangular as a slice of

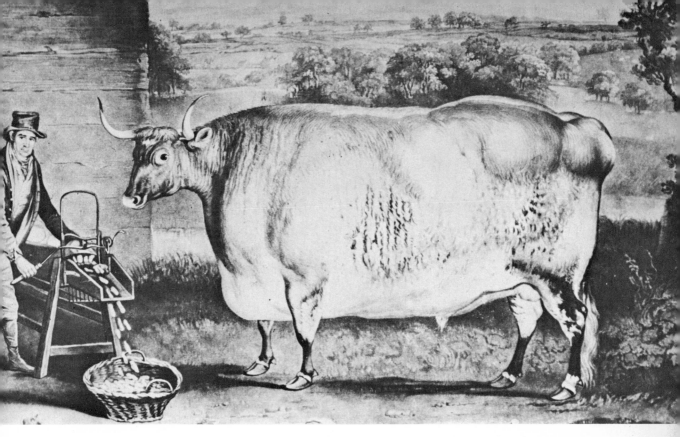

The "Newbus Ox", 1812. A Shorthorn/Highland cross.

toast, with tiny, short, slender legs, next to no neck and a head which could have belonged to a medium-sized sheep. But this very painting provides a clue to the accuracy of the artist's work. Her measurements are recorded, making a comparison between them and the picture possible. The picture can thus be shown to be badly out of proportion. The heifer is said to have been nearly 12 feet long and $5\frac{1}{2}$ feet high at the shoulder. But if the picture is correct in the matter of her length, then her height at the shoulder would be 7 feet. So either the artist or the man who took the measurements was wrong, and, as the latter worked to the nearest quarter-inch, it is unlikely to have been him.

The "Airedale" has at least fairly smooth contours. She is not disfigured by the unlikely bulges and rolls of fat which appear in the pictures of so many of her contemporaries. The "Newbus Ox" (1812) and the "Durham White Ox" (1813) are examples of the ridiculous convention. It is significant that both plates were made by William Ward, "engraver to their Royal Highnesses the Prince Regent and the Duke of York". Evidently an artist to be copied if one wanted to be in the fashion. The Durham bull, "Favourite" (1819) is so short and weak in his legs that any attempt to mount a cow would have been doomed to almost certain failure. The information attached to his portrait enthuses about his weight (2,018 lb.) and gives details of his breeding (he was a descendant of the sire who fathered the "Durham Ox") but, perhaps wisely, says nothing of his own performance as a sire. But again, he must have been better proportioned than his portrait implies.

That the pictures illustrate a vogue and are not true likenesses is demonstrated by a quotation that Mr. D. H. Boalch, the Rothamsted librarian who has catalogued the collection, has unearthed from the memoirs of Thomas Bewick, the great wood-engraver and one of the founders of British natural history. Bewick was a man of integrity. Concerning a commission he was given by a Durham breeder, he wrote:

> After I had made my drawings from the fat sheep, I soon saw that they were not approved, but that they were to be made like certain paintings shown to me. I observed to my employers that the paintings bore no resemblance to the animals whose figures I had made my drawings from; and that I would not alter mine to suit the paintings that were shown to me . . . my journey, as far as concerned these fat cattle makers, ended in nothing. I objected to lumps of fat here and there where I could not see it, at least not in so exaggerated a way as on the painting before me; so "I got my labour for my trouble." Many of the animals were, during this *rage* for fat cattle, fed up to as great a weight and bulk as it was possible for feeding to make them; but this was not enough; they were to be figured monstrously fat before the owners of them could be pleased. Painters were found who were quite subservient to this guidance, and nothing else would satisfy. Many of these paintings will mark the times and, by the exaggerated productions of the artists, serve to be laughed at when the folly and the self-interested motives which gave birth to them are done away with.

The honest Bewick was correct in his estimate that the craze for over-fat cattle was only temporary and would be found ludicrous by later generations. It is a relief to turn to one of his engravings in the Rothamsted collection. It is of one of the Chillingham wild bulls and shows a real animal, lean and active, pawing at the ground and with an evil glint in his eye, while his harem scampers for safety in the background. Obviously it was done from first-hand observation. Refreshing, too, is the realistic engraving by George Townley Stubbs, from a painting by George Stubbs, of two white bulls fighting, against a forest background. Here again is the work of a real artist, not of an unscrupulous ad-man.

The craze for monstrously obese animals soon petered out. By the 1840s a trend back to normal is discernible. It is true that "The Everingham Prize Cow", a Shorthorn, whose portrait was painted by W. H. Davis and engraved by J. Harris and which won a gold medal as the best beast exhibited at Smithfield in 1842, is still grossly fat, and her weight and dimensions are quoted with pride. But in the same year the portrait of "Eden", one of the Earl of Lonsdale's Shorthorn bulls, painted by R. Harrington and lithographed by Thomas Fairland, shows a fine, well-proportioned animal. The head still seems a little too small, but there are no exaggerated dumplings of fat and no trumpetings about size and weight.

Another interesting aspect of the fashion in gargantuan cattle is that it seems to have been confined very largely to Shorthorns. "A Herefordshire Bull", painted by R. Lawrence and engraved by F. Eginton in 1806, at the height of the folly, shows no exaggerations and is easily recognizable as a handsome, prototype Hereford, though somewhat different in conformation from those favoured at present. "A Fat Heifer", bred by Mr. W. Quartly, one of the founders of the Devon breed, and painted in 1820, depicts a beast the counterpart of which could be found in any Devon market today (apart from the unfashionable horns). Ellmann's "Sussex Bull", dated 1820, is

"Favourite", a Durham bull of 1818. An example of the improved Shorthorns bred by the Colling brothers.

A Hereford bull, 1806. Unlike many of the grotesque pictures of Shorthorns of the period, this portrait shows a handsome and well-proportioned animal, easily recognizable as a Hereford. It weighed 1648 lb at five years.

indeed a Sussex bull – lean, mean, well-proportioned and with no nonsense about him. "Dunlop bull", painted in 1813, shows a similarly commercial-type animal, an obvious ancestor of the modern Ayrshire, though with an emphasis on beef rather than dairy type.

So the Rothamsted collection does provide some insight into the ancestry and development of our modern breeds of cattle. We can see what a polled Aberdeen-Angus looked like in 1845. It is recognizable as an Aberdeen-Angus but considerably larger than the ones we know, and we may wonder whether the little West Highlanders, as illustrated in another picture, which stood only 3 feet 5 inches high at the age of five years, made their contribution to the modern breed. Probably so, for the caption tells us that the West Highland Kyloe "stands unrivalled as the first in the kingdom for quickness of grazing and superior quality of beef, and at all markets one third more is given for them unfed (according to their weight) than any other breed whatever." This particular heifer was "allowed by the judges to be the fattest ever seen, with the least coarse beef to its weight," but we may be assured that it is accurately depicted, for the painting is by the incorruptible Bewick.

* * *

The flaws thus revealed in the reliability of pictures of less than two hundred years ago give rise to the query: Are the older pictures and records to be trusted?

For instance, what of those pictures of Cretan acrobats turning somersaults over a bull's horns? The doubt is suggested because the bull in the now celebrated portrayal of that feat in a fresco on the walls of the palace of Knossos (see plate opposite page 64) is very like some of those suspect paintings of early nineteenth-century Shorthorns.

Let us examine some of the details. The body of this bull seems inordinately long, even allowing for the fact that it is fully extended. The forelegs are thrust out in front and the hind legs are extended behind as though the beast were in full career, stomach to ground.

But no, a bull does not run like that. He puts his head down and bunches up his shoulders and body, in order to place the maximum power behind his horns. The picture shows, in my opinion, a tethered bull, straining at his rope. He is reaching forward to his utmost extent, trying to reach the man standing tantalizingly in front of him. I would say he is tethered by the hind legs.

Even so, his legs are exceptionally short in proportion to his body. Is this accurate observation, or convention? If the former, is he a domestic bull? Perhaps one of a special breed of bull kept for purposes of displays in the arena of Knossos? Certainly he is sleeker and less shaggy than a wild bull should be. Also, perhaps, better fed. It has been suggested that Crete may have been cut off from mainland Greece at the end of the Ice Age before the aurochs moved in. That, apparently, is what happened to Ireland, where no indigenous wild bulls lived. Any bulls on Crete would therefore have been imported; and we are reminded of the sacred bulls which lived in the garden of Poseidon in Atlantis, according to Plato.

Again, if he were a domesticated bull, from a herd kept for the purpose, could he not have been a trained bull? It is a fact that bulls, at least some bulls, are not difficult to train. Many a bull has been trained to carry a rider, as a horse would, and the Romans, who had unlimited time at their resources, taught bulls to perform a repertoire of tricks. So, then, we are coming to the conclusion that this may have

A polled Aberdeenshire bull, "Banks of the Dee", 1845.

been a tethered bull, domesticated and trained. The feat of bull-leaping begins to look more credible.

And what of the colour of that Cretan bull? It is skewbald, which is surely the colour of a domestic animal, not a wild one? But here we are on less certain ground, as may be confirmed by a look at the rock paintings of Jabbaren. At least six of those cattle bear markings of brown and white, much like the bull of Knossos.

The fact that the naked hunters are trying to surround the cattle and are shooting at them with arrows indicates that these are wild animals. Nor would it be reasonable to suppose that the artist was doing anything more than depicting what he actually saw. Hence we must assume that black-and-white, brown-and-white, or black-brown-and-white were natural colours of the aurochs. The colour of the Knossos bull therefore tells nothing about whether or not it was trained or from domesticated stock.

120

The Saharan pictures also raise doubts about some of the statements made about the aurochs in the present century. Heinz Heck, who resurrected the aurochs in a series of brilliant genetical experiments (see page 16), says that the adult bull "was black with a yellow-white stripe along the back, while the cow was red-brown in colour with a darker neck". And so it is depicted in surviving paintings and engravings, notably in a much-reproduced painting discovered in an Augsburg antique shop in 1827. But evidently there was much variability. Perhaps the aurochs found in the forests of central Europe was a darker, northern form, while the African aurochs inclined towards lighter and more patchwork coloration. F. E. Zeuner (*A History of Domesticated Animals*) notes that "the summer coat was more sleek, especially in the southern races, whilst the winter coat was thick and somewhat curly". The Jabbaren animals appear to be sleek, as does the bull of Knossos.

A puzzling note is introduced by an Egyptian tomb painting of the time of Amenemhet, referred to earlier. A man is portrayed leading a bull which is pied, black-and-white, and stands no higher than his groin, say about 30 inches. This strange little animal is not a calf, for it appears to be sexually mature and it has long horns. What does it represent? Was there a dwarf race of aurochs? Or had the Egyptians at that early date succeeded not only in domesticating cattle but in establishing distinct breeds, including a dwarf one somewhat like our modern Dexter? An alternative explanation, that the size of the bull has been deliberately reduced by the artist in order to enhance the stature of the man is not really tenable, for the man in question is one of a row of undistinguished persons bearing gifts or tribute.

8
The Bull
in Modern Farming

"The bull is half the herd" is one of those old farming maxims which need qualifying. It all depends on the size of the herd. When I was a boy, our bull, who sired all the calves born in the village, was expected to cater for 50 or 60 cows. On many extensive ranches in the United States the proportion of bulls to cows is 3% – three bulls to 97 cows. On the estates that breed fighting bulls for the Spanish rings stud bulls are in the ratio of one to about 50 cows.

If a bull thus sires 50 calves in one year, in five years of service he will have fathered 250, or in 10 years 500. The average length of active life for a bull is somewhere between the two. Assuming equal proportions of each sex in his progeny, he could thus leave behind him from 125 to 250 sons, though not all would probably be of the same quality – there would be culls. And that hypothetical figure is borne out by actual records. That great ancestor of the Santa Gertrudis breed, "Monkey", of the King Ranch in Texas, sired just over 150 outstanding bulls in a service life of nine years (1923 to 1932). It is easy to see how breeds can claim (as many of them do) that all their animals are ultimately descended from one sire.

Artificial insemination has, of course, enormously extended the scope of a good bull. His semen can be used to inseminate thousands of cows, some of them on the far side of the world. It can be kept in cold store to be used long after he is dead – perhaps even on his own progeny to the nth generation, for in-breeding (or incest as it would be called in humans) is quite commonplace in the cattle-breeding world. A recent development in which a fertilized egg or embryo fetus is removed from a cow and implanted into the uterus of a foster mother can extend the influence of the sire still further, for the purpose of the operation is to allow the donor cow, who is of the highest quality, to produce more progeny than would be possible by her unaided efforts.

Santa Gertrudis bull. Note "Running W", the brand mark of the King Ranch, Texas.

There are, of course, inherent dangers in this developing programme. Weaknesses as well as desirable characteristics may be inherited, and cattle-breeders have to be constantly on the watch for them. A bull who is found to be transmitting a fault can do far more damage when siring a thousand calves a year than when fathering 50. So far nothing irrevocable has happened, but geneticists, aware of the hazard, are supporting schemes to preserve the older and less improved breeds, such as the Longhorn (both English and Texan), as banks of genes of the old virtues such as hardiness, stamina and resistance to disease, against the time when they may be needed.

In earlier chapters we have noted how breeders, in past times and in various countries, have selected their breeding animals for a variety of points, some of which strike us as bizarre. Thus in England within my own lifetime we tended to breed for colour; in parts of Africa and India the most esteemed criterion was a pair of huge horns; Spanish fighting bulls and those on the Camargue are selected for their fighting qualities; and so on. In India, far back in legendary times, it seems that the need for careful selection of breeding sires was appreciated, for, as described on page 34, the unknown king who originated the custom of turning Brahmini bulls loose and dedicating them to Siva, so that they should sire worthy calves on the village cows, decreed that only the best bulls should be chosen.

As already noted, since then we have come to realize that many qualities other than the obvious ones are transmitted through the male line. Indeed, it is fair to state that nearly all qualities are inherited equally from the male and female sides, though there are, of course, individual variations.

The characteristics which farmers and commercial cattle-breeders value in cattle are as follows:

1. *Milk production*; of particular importance in dairy cattle but of some significance in beef animals, for a beef cow should produce enough milk to keep her calf for six months or so.

2. *Butterfat content of milk*; the milk of beef cows, being small in quantity, is usually rich in butterfat, but dairy cows giving large yields of milk may have difficulty in maintaining acceptable standards of butterfat and SNF (solids-not-fat). Dairy bulls have shown their ability to transmit this quality to their female progeny.

3. *Fertility*.

4. *Mothering ability*; more important in beef cows, which suckle their calves for long periods, than in dairy animals.

5. *Colour*; of less importance today than formerly, though some breeds reject certain colours. For example, there is a separate breed society for red-and-white Friesians, though red-and-white animals turn up from time to time in pure black-and-white herds.

6. *Disposition*; not of great importance if other characteristics are right, but most breeders would give preference to an animal with a placid disposition, as against a nervous one. On the other hand, breeders of fighting bulls select deliberately for a fiery and pugnacious temperament.

7. *Conformation*; awards at shows are often made on this quality alone, and every breeder of pure-bred cattle likes to have animals which conform to the breed type. Conformation is basically of greater importance in beef breeds than in dairy, for, in the end, the conformation of a beef carcase has a direct commercial value, whereas in dairy cattle it is simply an indication of certain other qualities, such as milk production capacity, which experience has taught breeders to associate with it.

8. *Longevity*; of greater importance with dairy breeds, though a beef cow who can successfully produce and rear a calf annually for 12 years or more is worth having.

9. *Early maturity*; in dairy cattle a cow capable of producing a calf, followed by a useful lactation, at the age of two years instead of three or four (and Jerseys habitually do this), can obviously save her owner the cost of a year's unproductive keep.

10. *Rate of liveweight gain*; this is not quite the same thing as early maturity, though it amounts to something similar. In beef cattle it is of prime importance. The beef producer sets as his target a certain weight at which each animal is to be marketed. The animal which arrives there several weeks ahead of its mates is clearly a winner, from its owner's point of view. Some beef cattle put on weight at rates of from 2 to 4 lb a day.

11. *Food conversion efficiency*; the rate at which an animal gains weight is obviously connected with the standard of the ration fed to it, but some animals gain weight more quickly than others on identical rations.

12. *Quality of meat*; of importance only in beef. However, much meat now comes from surplus animals in dairy herds, so bulls for mating with dairy cows with a view to beef production from the progeny are selected to correct faults in the dairy animals, among other criteria. Thus, in Britain beef with yellow fat, such as Channel Island cattle produce, is unpopular with consumers, so bulls with white-fatted flesh are chosen to mate with Guernsey and Jersey cows.

13. *Proportion of meat to bone*; a consideration of obvious importance to the butcher and therefore to the farmer who sells the carcase.

14. *Tolerance of heat and cold*; a good general recommendation of importance to those who want to keep cattle under extremes of climate.

All of these qualities have been shown to be hereditary to some extent, and heritable from the sire as well as from the dam. That is not to say that they depend entirely on heredity. The ratio is variable. It has been said that milk production depends 20% on heredity and 80% on food, environment and management. Accepting that figure, and assuming that the bull is responsible for half the heredity, we may also assume that a really good cow may in her lifetime produce, say, 20,000 gallons of milk. 10% of that total would be 2,000 gallons, a bonus attributable to the bull. It is a worthwhile consideration.

But how do we know what qualities a bull is going to transmit to his offspring? If we are judging by colour, appearance and conformation only, the task is not difficult. On page 106 is a short account of the birth of one of the great ancestors of the Hereford breed. Both Mr. Tully, the owner, and his herdsman recognized it as a magnificent calf as soon as they saw it. But any ability to produce more milk which a bull may have transmitted to his female progeny will not become evident until the heifers have themselves produced calves and completed their first lactation. That is how the value of a bull is now assessed. After he has finished an initial bout of service and has sired a sizeable group of progeny (heifers where a dairy bull is concerned) he is put out to grass for a few years, until it is possible to measure the performance of his offspring. When he has passed this test, he is a Proven Sire. Although he will then be three or four years older, he should still have several years of service before him. And, of course, his semen can be kept frozen for use, if desired, after he is dead.

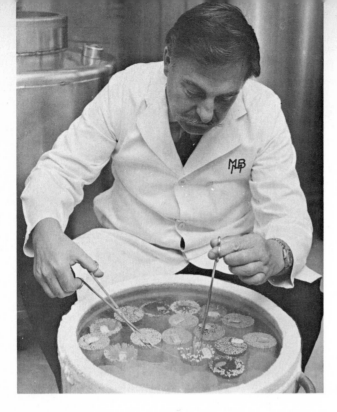

At a Milk Marketing Board's Cattle Breeding Centre, chief-technician W. Stork fills a deep-frozen transfer vessel with colour-coded doses of semen.

The programme can be varied to suit circumstances. Testing for inherited milk-producing capacity covers the longest period, for the heifers have to grow to maturity before the tests can even begin. Results may be obtained from beef cattle, in trials of their rate of growth and food conversion efficiency, at an earlier date. Account must also be taken of the contribution provided by the dam. And it is worth remembering that the first cross between two pure-bred animals is endowed with what is termed "hybrid vigour", which means that the young animal is better than the average of his two parents. This excellence is not always passed on to future generations.

Incidentally, a word about "pedigree" may be appropriate here. "Pedigree" means simply that the ancestry of the animal has been recorded for several generations. It is *not* synonymous with "pure-bred", although it is often used as though it were. In practice, few breeders bother to keep the pedigrees of any other than pure-bred animals, but pedigree mongrels are perfectly possible and are not a contradiction in terms. Most pedigrees are reliable, but some are not. Just as paternity, in the human species, depends ultimately on the testimony of one woman, so in the cattle world it depends on the word of a farmer. Most farmers are to be trusted.

Ever since men started to interfere with cattle and to exploit them for their own purposes, the lot of the bull has been, in general, an unenviable one. It is true that in an earlier chapter we quote the idyllic life of a Texan bull on free range with a harem of heifers as a dreamer's vision of Paradise, but bulls on free range are the exception

126

in the modern world. Only where vast unfenced horizons exist, as in Australia and western America and Canada, is it permissible for bulls to roam at large. In the restricted landscapes of western Europe, especially in the vicinity of urban conglomerations, a bull loose in a meadow is anathema to all who pass by, and particularly to any who think they have the right to cross that meadow.

So the bull is confined like a criminal. In the 1930s, when the economic depression was still unchecked and half the countryside was derelict, we used to run a young bull on the downs with a bunch of heifers for a few months, having first made sure that the fences were sound. When he had done service there, he came home to the farmyard and lived in a compartment in the barn. Twice a day regularly he went into the yard for water and exercise, with visits from cows an interesting bonus. It could not have been too bad a life, though somewhat restricted and boring.

I remember that at one stage, when they were first introduced, we bought one of those bull tethers, which allows the bull to tread a circular course around a peg anchored in a meadow, but our bull didn't appreciate it one bit. Perhaps the sight of distant horizons, which he might not pass, and green fields out of bounds over the hedge unsettled him. Anyway, he was happier in his familiar pen in the barn. Maybe it was because he was middle-aged before the tether was introduced and so was too old to adapt. Nowadays tethers are the lot of most bulls in lowland Britain. For most farmers now – 90% or more in some districts – have their cows artificially inseminated. And the bulls that serve them live on tethers at artificial insemination or cattle-breeding centres.

The modern development of artificial insemination (commonly known as A.I.) began in Russia, where it was first applied on a practical scale in 1922. In earlier centuries experiments had been made in several countries, notably England and Italy, and apparently Arabs used the technique in breeding horses back in the Middle Ages. Interest having been aroused by the Russian success, similar investigations were initiated in western countries in the 1930s, the pioneers in Britain being Sir John Hammond and Dr. Walton. The first commercial A.I. service in Britain was started at Cambridge in 1942.

In 1944 the Milk Marketing Board prepared a plan to cover the whole of England and Wales with a network of A.I. stations. It picked the areas with the greatest concentration of dairy cows and allocated stations to those which had 60,000 cows within a reasonable radius. The plan was to place "30 bulls a centre (the maximum size because of foot-and-mouth disease risks); an estimate that ultimately 50% of the cows in the area would be offered for A.I.; an estimate of 1,000 cows inseminated from each bull annually".

While the first clause was adhered to, the estimates in the other two proved wildly pessimistic. By 1959 the Milk Marketing Board was able to report that "already demand in some areas has resulted in more than 90 cows in every 100 being inseminated and, thanks to technical progress in dilution rates, the use of bulls is already more than twice the original estimate".

By that time the Board had established 24 stations, and in addition in the early days, before the Board's scheme had been launched, seven other private stations had been founded and still function. They are at Cambridge, Reading, Ruthin, Dartington Hall, Lyndhurst (Hampshire), Avoncroft (Worcestershire) and Ilminster (Somerset). There may be a passing interest in a personal reminiscence of mine. When visiting Danish farms in 1949 I found a farmer on the island of Zealand (Sjaelland) operating his own insemination programme, using semen from his own bull, injecting it into his cows and washing out the test-tubes in the kitchen sink!

At a cattle-breeding centre the resident bulls are put out to pasture, on tether, most days, and an impressive sight they form – 30 or so fine bulls grouped in a comparatively small space, though out of each other's reach. This last must be a considerable hardship to the individual bull, whose natural instinct is to regard other bovine males as his rivals and to engage in bouts to show who is master. They eye each other with malice and indulge in the occasional frustrated blare.

When called upon to do their duty, the exercise amounts to masturbation. The bull is excited by a "teaser" cow, whose role is to stimulate him to sexual activity. This she does while standing in a mounting frame. At the critical moment a technician interposes an artificial vagina between the bull and the cow. This vagina is a thick rubber tube, well lubricated and kept at the proper temperature and pressure by an enclosing water-jacket. The semen is collected in a glass phial at the end and taken off for dilution and either immediate use or storage. The bull then returns to the pasture.

The semen from one bull is now used, in some instances, to inseminate as many as 1,000 cows a year, as well as allowing for a surplus to be placed in deep freeze. The proportion of successful inseminations at the first service is 67–70%, though more in some instances. A.I. proved so popular that, from its beginning in 1944, the Milk Marketing Board insemination service recorded 10 million calves by 1959, and achieved a record of 25 million by 1965.

(Right above) *Pedigree bulls are exercised prior to their donation of semen. This method of exercise is used particularly in winter, when the bulls are housed for the rest of the day.*
(Right below) *Seven-year-old Charolais bull, "Apollou" at a Cattle Breeding Centre.*

128

The technique of deep-freezing semen imposed formidable problems at first. In the early days semen was frozen in dry ice, but from 1963 onwards liquid nitrogen, at a temperature of $-193°C$ has been used and is more satisfactory. Traffic in frozen semen is now international and extensive. A draft document prepared by the F.A.O. in 1966 showed no fewer than 39 countries had even enacted detailed legislation controlling the movement of animal semen.

One important advantage of A.I. over natural service is that it imposes a check on venereal disease, which is a problem with cattle as with humans. At least four major diseases, including the dreaded brucellosis (which can be passed to humans), can be transmitted venereally. Certain countries which prohibit the importation of live-stock, for fear of disease, permit the importation of semen.

In countries and regions where the practice of artificial insemination is now well established, the ratio of artificial inseminations to natural services does not alter much. That is, there are few changes within a given area, though there is much variation from area to area, depending on the local type of animal husbandry. In dairying regions the incidence of A.I. is high, in stock-breeding regions somewhat lower. This is closely linked to the problem of catching the cow on heat. Heat periods, when the cow is receptive to the bull, occur at intervals of about 20 days and are of very short duration. In dairy herds, where the herdsman has his stock under fairly constant observation, he usually manages to detect cows on heat without much difficulty. In free-ranging herds, and particularly with maiden heifers, it is virtually impossible. The practice therefore is to run a bull with herds on free range and to use A.I. with dairy cows and others which are kept under close surveillance.

* * *

From time to time in this book steers have been mentioned. A steer is a castrated bull, and castration is the fate that overtakes most bull calves. A steer, ox or bullock not only loses his sexual ability, he also develops certain secondary characteristics which place him, in effect, in neutral territory between male and female. He does not, for instance, develop the massive shoulders and neck muscles of the bull; he tends to run to fat rather than muscle. He is smaller, lighter and much more docile than a bull. He has a total lack of interest in females. He tends to eat less but grows more slowly and, in general, is less economical to feed where meat production is the criterion, though,

(Left) *Bull-riding at the Calgary Stampede.*

"Aldersend Galaxy", *champion Hereford bull at the Royal Welsh Show, 1970.*

of course, that is an advantage when he is kept for draught work. When slaughtered, his carcase has a higher proportion of fat to lean than does a bull carcase.

With this in mind, it seems rather surprising that castration is such a common practice. Prejudice and convention are partly responsible. In the past bull beef meant to most consumers the flesh of animals who had put in an extensive period of service and were slaughtered in their declining years. It had a tendency to be tough, dark-coloured and rather strong in flavour. But these defects do not occur in bulls slaughtered at the age of about 20 months, as is usual nowadays with steers programme-fed to produce "baby-beef". Such immature bulls have considerable advantages over steers in food conversion rates and rates of liveweight gain, a fact that has been appreciated for a long time in continental Europe but is only just becoming realized in Britain.

130

A survey in 1973 showed that 53% of all beef coming to the market in Italy and 44% in West Germany was derived from bulls. In West Germany the total beef production from steers had dropped to 2% (the balance being made up of cow and heifer beef); in the Netherlands steers had practically disappeared. In Britain at the same period, out of 2,250,000 slaughtered for beef in the previous year, only 10,680 were entire bulls.

The year 1973 saw the beginning of a campaign, which has so far proved not particularly successful, to promote the production of bull beef. Sundry trials were conducted to determine its superiority over steer beef. In an exercise conducted by the Meat and Livestock Commission bulls showed a daily gain in weight 13.4% higher than steers kept under identical conditions. The advantage in food cost, per pound of weight gained, was 10.6%. In this trial the bulls arrived at the target weight 19 days earlier than the steers and so showed a considerably greater margin of profit.

In a similar trial by the Irish Research Institute by the time the steers had reached 323 kg in weight the bulls were up to 353 kg. The advantage to the bulls in meat produced was, in this instance, 35.1%. In experiments in the beef unit of the National Agricultural Centre at Stoneleigh, Warwickshire, the bulls achieved a 9.1% advantage in liveweight gain, besides producing a higher proportion of lean meat on their carcase. Butchers testified that "in flavour, juiciness and overall acceptability no consistent differences had been found between bull and steer beef."

In a Bull Beef Conference which I attended at Reading University in April, 1973, Mr. Tom Fox, a Warwickshire farmer, described some of the practical problems of keeping and fattening young bulls in batches. In his initial trial he matched 55 bulls against 55 steers on a semi-intensive system involving autumn grazing before going into fattening yards. He found that the bulls were, when grazing, less excitable than the steers, and when they entered the yards they had put on about 56 lb extra weight. They maintained their superiority throughout the fattening period, despite considerable riding, and were ready for slaughter earlier. The inspectors said that the carcases lacked finish, and one-third of them were graded low. Even so, they gave a considerably higher margin of profit than did the steers.

Mr. Fox said that the difference in behaviour between the bulls and steers was striking. Whereas the steers grazed as a herd, the bulls spread themselves over the entire field, very rarely associating with each other. The steers came as a bunch to greet visitors and showed lively interest, whereas the bulls remained indifferent, indeed walking away when approached. The bulls presented no management problems, however, and walked quietly from field to field when necessary. When housed at the end of summer the bulls experienced a disturbed period for about a week, with much riding and mounting taking place, but the general rate of gain in weight was not arrested. As the bulls settled down to concentrate feeding they began to pull even further ahead of the steers. Their better condition was even apparent visually.

In a second trial on the same farm similar results were recorded. Again no problems from dangerous behaviour occurred, except that this batch contained one rogue bull. This animal was soon withdrawn from the herd and housed, after which there was no further trouble. An attempt to mix two lots of bulls, however, proved something of a disaster. They rode each other constantly for about a fortnight until they were thoroughly exhausted. As a result, they not only failed to put on weight but actually lost some.

Mr. J. W. Frater, a Northumberland farmer who conducted a similar trial between bulls and steers from a single-suckled herd, was also agreeably surprised at the ease of management, the young bulls being as quiet as their steered herd-mates. He too recorded a consistent advantage in gain in weight by the bulls. The Grassland Research Institute at Hurley, Berkshire, has also experimented with grazing bulls. Although the bulls have been observed to spend much more time idling and less in grazing than the steers, their performance has not suffered. Given plenty of good grazing, they put on the optimum amount of weight and then benefit from high-energy finishing rations.

A major handicap to the production of bull beef in a densely-populated country such as Britain is the possible hazard involved in keeping considerable numbers of bulls loose out-of-doors. It is true that these are young bulls which have not developed the crusty temperament of many mature bulls, but they are nevertheless bulls and need to be treated with caution from about the age of six months. Many farms are fragmented to the extent that cattle moved between fields need to traverse a public highway. And many fields have public footpaths crossing them. These, though, are not universal problems, and where conditions are favourable many more entire bulls will undoubtedly be kept for beef in the future.

9

The Nature of a Bull

For an observer in the more thickly populated parts of the world to study the natural behaviour of bulls is difficult, for the reason that most of the bulls he is likely to see are kept under wholly unnatural conditions. Moreover, they are all domesticated bulls, bred through many generations to emphasize certain characteristics which are of commercial importance to their owners but which remove them further and further from the primitive types from which they evolved. To appreciate the role of the bull in the herd, and to understand to some small degree what it is like to be a bull, we need to look at bulls in the wild.

The best opportunity for so doing in Britain is provided by the Chillingham herd of wild white cattle in Northumberland, to which several references have already been made. In a fascinating account of these cattle in his *A Survey of the Agriculture of Northumberland*, Professor H. C. Pawson, gives the following description of the place of the bull in the herd:

> One of the most interesting features of this "natural" herd is the emergence and reign of what is known as the "king" bull, who alone serves the cows. The "king", or leader of the herd, establishes his right of absolute monarchy by combat and holds his dominant position until he is defeated in battle and is then temporarily banished from the herd and the successful bull enters into his "reign". The present "king" bull is seven years old (1959). When a bull aspires to be "king" he bellows loudly, paws the ground and seeks to incite the "reigning" monarch to do battle. Several short attacks may ensue, with short grazing intervals, until finally, each watching for the other to be off-guard, one after several clashes retires defeated. The vanquished bull lives separately from the herd for a long time, if not out of sight, then at a safe distance. The cutting up of the turf bears witness to the conflicts which take place, for the bulls kneel on their forelegs, throwing the turf over their heads when they offer a challenge. Occasionally the older monarch may regain his position, but it is only a temporary success, for old age inevitably yields to youth. Death is unusual in the struggle for supremacy but does occasionally take place.

"Wild Cattle of Chillingham"; a painting by Basil Bradley, 1890.

Professor Pawson provides some additional items of information.

> The cattle feed mainly in the evening and when they move do so in file, the "king" leading, cows and calves forming the centre, and other bulls to the rear . . .
>
> The calf is dropped in a secluded spot and remains hidden, being suckled two or three times daily, until it is brought into the herd by the dam at about a week to a fortnight old, being first met by the "king" bull, who escorts them in person, when the mother and new arrival are duly inspected and approved by the other ladies of the herd . . .
>
> If thoroughly alarmed, e.g. by a pack of fox-hounds, the herd stampedes in a well-arranged formation of cows in front, calves next, then the bulls, with the "king" bull this time in the rear of all.

The picture that emerges is a quite impressive and attractive one of a true patriarch, controlling and protecting his herd in a thoroughly dignified and commendable manner. Wherever cattle are allowed adequate scope to form their own social communities, the same pattern appears. And the behaviour of allied bovine species tends to be similar.

In an earlier chapter we noted that on the great migrations of American bison, in the days when the prairies were oceans of grass, the lead was generally taken by an experienced old cow, but that applied only to migration time. In the mating season the hordes split up into smaller herds, each under the dominance of a mature male. As with so many other animals, rival males fought for the supremacy. Sometimes a simple show of aggression was sufficient to send the challenger into retreat. The bulls would approach each other, bellowing and shaking their heads. When a fight ensued the bulls lowered their heads, pressed their foreheads together and tried to wound their adversary by quick upward thrusts with their horns. Sometimes a severe wound resulted, but more often the weaker animal, finding he was likely to lose, gave up the struggle before much damage was done.

These combats took place in July and August, the mating season. The leadership argument settled, the victorious bull would take charge of the herd for a few months, leading it about and being the first to engage in any activity, from drinking to wallowing. The rest respectfully stood aside till the old man had finished. In winter, after the migration, the bulls assembled in male-only groups and remained so until the next mating season. The calves were born in late spring and were soon able to travel with their mothers. If they were attacked by predators, the whole herd would rally to the defence.

In his book *Cattle Raising on the Plains of North America* (written in 1882) Walter Baron von Richthofen includes some notes on the behaviour of the great herds of cattle, mostly Texas Longhorns though already with some improvements due to the introduction of European breeds, which were taking the place of the vanishing bison on the prairies.

> Between the domestic or stable-reared cattle of the Eastern states and of Europe, and those reared on the Western prairies, there exists a great difference. Although the latter cannot strictly be called wild, yet they have peculiarities in their nature common to the buffalo. For instance, they will run away if they see somebody on foot. A cow will often defend her calf when it is caught by the lasso; they move about in families, grazing and herding together, and the attachment of a cow to her calf, and vice versa, is much greater than that of the domestic animal. Here and there one can watch groups of families where the offspring of three or four generations have never been separated. The mother always retains her authority, and even punishes her children and grandchildren, though they may be much larger than herself; but in the defense of families the female yields precedence to the male . . .

About noon herds move towards their watering places, where they remain for two or three hours, and then, like buffalo, march back in single file to their favourite pasture grounds. In summer they seldom graze farther than five or six miles from water, while in winter they spread over more territory, often remaining two or three days without water, and even eating snow for drink. During a heavy snow-storm groups and families gather together in small herds and, with their backs to the storm, shelter one another . .

African buffaloes assemble in herds of perhaps a hundred individuals or even more. A herd comprises buffaloes of all ages and both sexes, with about three times as many adult cows as bulls. At mating time there are fights between the males, which, however, stop short of doing much harm to each other. The losers drift away and form bachelor groups, which hang about on the fringes of the main herd. When the herd is on the move, these stalwart bulls bring up the rear and chase off any predatory animals which may have hostile ideas in their heads. The oldest bulls of all often wander off and live entirely solitary lives.

Much the same seems to be true of the Indian buffaloes, though so few are now left in the wild that their social behaviour is difficult to determine. Big, solitary males are often observed away from the main herds, and Balakrishna Seshadri (*The Twilight of India's Wild Life*) suggests two alternative explanations. One is that the males habitually live away from the females and immature animals except in the mating season. The other, which seems to me the more likely, is that these are bulls that have got the worst of a battle with a rival and so have been driven out of the herd. Support for the second theory may be found in the fact that the solitary buffalo bulls often mate with domestic buffalo cows grazing in their vicinity – an activity to which the herdsmen have no objection, as the calves tend to be bigger and stronger. Seshadri describes how, when a wild bull arrives, among his first actions is to kill off all the domestic bulls he can find. To forestall this disaster, the villagers castrate their domestic bulls, after which the intruder takes no notice of them.

He heard of one instance of a wild bull killing two domestic bulls when he joined a herd, upon which the other four domestic bulls took to the jungle. The wild bull remained with the herd for six months, after which he too disappeared, leaving the villagers without a sire.

He adds that such a bull will become quite tame during the time he is with a domestic herd. Forest bulls take no notice of other domestic animals or of children herding the cows, but they react strongly to the presence of an adult human. The villagers find that, when a wild buffalo bull is in attendance, such large carnivores as tigers and leopards leave the herd severely alone. A tiger will very seldom attack a full-grown wild buffalo, bull or cow, though sometimes two tigers working in concert will attempt it.

The gaur, that other giant bull of India and the East, apparently lives in much smaller herds, seldom of more than 20 individuals and usually much less. As it is a shy creature, lurking in forests by day, and as it has also become rare, little is known of its social habits.

Although the musk-ox is not a true member of the cattle family, it is sufficiently ox-like to be included in this book. Its social behaviour is interesting. When danger threatens a herd all the adult members instinctively form a circle, flanks inwards, heads outwards, around the calves. They thus present an unbroken rampart of sharp horns to the enemy, usually wolves, although even wolves are chary about attacking musk-oxen. The phalanx keeps in constant motion, wheeling about its axis, with the horns perpetually swinging. An incautious wolf may be swept into the air, to fall within the wall and be trampled to death.

In the mating season, which is summer, the bulls engage in apparently ferocious combats, although little damage results as a rule.

Musk-oxen are now being domesticated, in Canada, Alaska and Greenland, primarily for their wonderfully soft wool, known as qiviut. As man becomes more familiar with them they are revealed as intelligent and inquisitive animals, with many endearing traits. For instance, they soon learn to enjoy immensely a game of pushball, using a large ball with a diameter almost equal to their height. They also play "king of the castle", trying to push one another off a mound or other eminence, like lambs on a bale of straw. In the *National Geographic Magazine* (Vol. 137, No. 6, June, 1970) John J. Teal describes how domesticated musk-oxen dealt with an intruding dog in their pen. Instead of forming a defensive circle, they chased the dog around the corral in a kind of relay. As the leading pursuer tired another would move up to take its place, so that the frightened dog constantly had a fresh enemy on his tail and had to continue moving at full speed in order to keep clear. Fearing for the life of the dog, the herdsman stepped in front of the galloping musk-oxen and shouted "Halt!" They obediently did so, and the dog escaped.

Their willingness to stop at a word of command brings me to some personal reminiscences of encounters and experiences with bulls.

As I have said, when I was in my teens I had charge of a fine Shorthorn bull who, unfortunately, had to spend much of the day chained in a stall in an old thatched barn. Twice a day he emerged for a drink at the water trough in the yard and a half-hour's exercise – though he often wanted to go back to his stall before the half-hour was up. At other times he came out to serve cows. It was a cosy enough existence, but boring. I used to feel sorry for him and talked to him a lot as I cleaned out his stall and prepared his meals. Of course, he came to know me well.

In those days of makeshift farming, the bull's stall was haphazardly planned. To release him, I had to stand on the edge of the wooden manger, unfasten the chain around his neck and then step back smartly before he swung his head around to move out. One morning I did this as usual, stepped on the edge of a displaced cobble-stone in the pen's floor and went down in a heap. One of my ankles was so badly sprained that I couldn't put my foot to ground for days. So there I was, lying helpless almost beneath the bull who, now loose, was about to move across to the doorway that led into the yard.

He paused, looked down at me and sniffed. The next move, I knew, would be to give me a tentative prod with his horns or forehead, and then I would be in dire trouble. I raised my voice and commanded him firmly, "Out! Out, you old rascal!" Obediently he turned and walked quietly to the yard. I crawled to the side of the pen and raised myself upright, sweating. But there was nothing malicious about that bull.

Of course, the relationship between us was personal. He knew me, and I knew him, as an individual. Would he have behaved in the same way with any person? No. We had one dairyman, who did not stay long, who was terrified of bulls. And the bulls knew it. The bull we had then, of whom the dairyman was supposed to be in charge, would follow him menacingly around the yard, tossing his head and showing the whites of his eyes. The dairyman made matters worse by using his stick too freely. It was war between them.

Earlier I gave a brief account of the behaviour of wild Indian buffalo bulls who join herds of domestic buffaloes on the outskirts of villages in order to mate with the cows. The wild bulls pay no attention to children who are supposed to be in attendance on the herds but show alarm and resentment when an adult approaches. In a lifetime on a farm and associating with animals in many parts of the world I have only once known an animal deliberately to attack a small child. That was a supposedly placid and senile matron of a cow, too old to travel with the herd, who charged one of my little daughters, aged four, when she ventured into the paddock. I can only suppose that senility had temporarily upset the balance of that poor old cow's mind.

I remember that one market day morning when a dozen or two villagers were making their way down the village street towards the bus stop a neighbour's Friesian bull escaped. He suddenly appeared in the road and came trotting along, snorting, bellowing and tossing his great head. No crowd under sudden machine-gun fire ever dispersed more rapidly. Refuge was taken behind hedges and garden gates and

The bull that had the author at his mercy.

through any front doors that happened to be unlocked. Within seconds the road was deserted, apart from the bull.

My wife, in our home not far from the bus stop, heard the commotion and went out to see what it was about. Seeing the bull, she dashed back into the house for a walking-stick; then ran out and confronted him. She just stood there, in the middle of the road, waving her stick and telling him to stop. Of course, he stopped. Then she advanced towards him, still talking to him. He turned round and retreated, back to the safety of the yard, where his anxious owner had just discovered his absence. The refugees emerged and resumed their walk to the bus stop, now equipped with a good topic of conversation for the bus journey. Did my wife get due credit for being heroic? Not really. Some people are afraid of bulls and some are not. It was lucky that she was one of those who aren't.

Such tactics would work with most bulls. Stand your ground, and the bull will stop. Advance towards him, and he will retreat. Talk to him and, even though he may not understand the words, he will recognise an authoritative tone of voice.

Much depends on the breed of bull and his past experience with the human race. Not long ago I and some grandchildren went picking mushrooms in a meadow where a big Hereford bull was grazing. We never gave him a second thought. But if that had been a Jersey bull I would not have ventured into the field without a stout stick, and I would have kept a wary eye on him all the time. At agricultural shows a Hereford bull will enter the ring led by a piece of rope with a small child holding the other end. But the Jersey bull who follows him will need two men grasping poles linked by chains to the ring in his nose to hold him. Highlanders, despite their formidable horns, are as gentle as lambs. Most of the beef breed bulls are reasonably placid, though I did not like the look of that Santa Gertrudis bull who tested a gate on Texas ranch in a vain attempt to get at me as described earlier.

Mr. Tom Fox, whose experiences with keeping young bulls for beef are quoted in a previous chapter, found in his first two experiments only one rogue bull out of over eighty. Another expert has put the incidence of difficult bulls at not more than one to forty, but I am inclined to think that is too high.

Even fighting bulls, bred for generations for their pugnacious qualities, are not all aggressive. Quite a fair proportion of the bulls that appear in Spanish bull-rings fail to react in the way expected. Instead of roaring in, charging at the first object which moves and eager for a fight, they turn around and try to retreat the way they came. Or they trot around the ring, looking for another way of escape. The spectators dub them cowards, but they are not. They are sensible bulls, not liking the place where they find themselves. They want to return to their familiar pastures.

A bull's natural place is with the herd, as its master. He will do battle with other bulls for the mastery, though seldom to the point of killing. He will do battle for the herd against predators. Those incidents apart, he is not an over-aggressive animal. He is gentle with his cows and tolerant with their calves. Read again the account, on page 134, of the attractive behaviour of the bull of the Chillingham herd, who inspects each new calf and leads it to be introduced to the herd.

The young adolescent males have their place in the scheme of things. When the herd is on the move, to new pastures, they bring up the rear, prepared to attack any predators who may have designs on straggling calves. Their time will come, when one of the strongest will challenge the old bull for the supremacy of the herd. In the meantime, they have a function to fulfil, and they perform their duties with restraint and dignity, traits they carry over into the restricted, frustrating conditions of domesticated life. On page 131 is an account of how groups of young bulls are kept together on pastures. Each remains proud and aloof, taking little notice of his fellows. They are individualistic. They respect each other's need for such privacy and living space as is possible in a limited area. Their only common vice seems to be homosexuality, which is not rare among young human males who are thrown together in tight groups for longish periods.

*   *   *

140

On virtually all counts, the bull emerges from this survey as a nobler creature than the humans who exploit him. One of the greatest of all paintings of bulls is *Gordale Scar*, by James Ward (1769–1859). On the floor of a deep chasm, hemmed in by dark crags and with thunder clouds rolling overhead, a white bull stands proud and vigilant as he guards his herd. Some of his cows are grazing, some sitting down and chewing the cud, some are suckling their calves. There are other animals in the valley, notably a herd of deer. Two of the stags are testing their antlers on each other, but none of the others takes any notice. It is a scene of idyllic tranquillity, *because there is no man there.*

Gaze at the picture and consider what would happen if a man suddenly appeared. Every animal would be immediately alert and in flight. With luck he might see the last of them disappearing among the rocks. And the precipices would reverberate with the echoes of his shouts or his gun.

The intrusion of no other animal would provoke the same reaction. Even a predator would be regarded warily but would not cause the herds to panic. The antelopes, zebras, giraffes, wildebeeste and other animals of the African plains co-exist with the lions, cheetahs and hyenas that prey on them. The presence of the predators keeps them alert, but they know instinctively that there will be no wanton killing. Once a cheetah has killed for its meal, the herd from which it has taken a member will be safe for a time. Only man kills more than he needs, for sport or blood-lust.

Men have treated bulls far worse than bulls have treated men. They have taken away from innumerable bulls their masculinity, by castration. They have baited them cruelly for sport. They still kill thousands annually in the ritual spectacle of the bull-ring. Simply because they can devise no other way of controlling them they confine these splendid animals, whose natural instinct is to roam freely over plains and through forests with their herds, in concrete, iron-barred cells. There is no indignity they have not heaped upon them, and yet they fear their victims. The bull is one of the few animals, ruthlessly exploited by man, who, given the chance, has the power to retaliate.

Daniel P. Mannix in *Those About to Die* describes the death of a bull in a Roman arena. Having been mortally wounded, the bull has turned and caught one of his tormentors unawares. He has tossed and gored him, and now the man lies dead on the sand. The bull walks over to inspect his adversary, sniffing at the blood and then proudly raising his head. So he gazes for a long defiant minute at the excited spectators until his legs collapse and he falls dead.

He had not wanted to be there. He had been committed, against his will, to a conflict he would have avoided, but he had acquitted himself well. His attitude towards his persecutors was contemptuous. He maintained his dignity to the end. Which was the nobler, the dying bull or the hooting rabble in the stands?

C. S. Lewis, discussing animal pain in his book *The Problem of Pain*, surveys the possibility of a paradise where the lion and the lamb would be at peace.

> But if there is a rudimentary Leonine self, to that also God can give a "body" as it pleases Him – a body no longer living by the destruction of the lamb, yet richly leonine in the sense that it also expressed whatever energy and splendour and exulting power dwelled within the visible lion on this earth . . . I think the lion, when he has ceased to be dangerous, will still be awful. . . . There will still be something like the shaking of a golden mane; and often the good Duke will say, "Let him roar again".

May there not also be a matching taurine presence – a valiant, possessive, alert, virile, magnificent bull, proudly standing guard over the Elysian pastures?

Some have imagined a Last Judgment in which the judges of the human race are animals. There, arrayed to weigh the evidence for and against us, will be the trapped beavers, the whales killed by explosive shells, the murdered bisons, the clubbed seals, the exterminated dodos, the horses shattered in human wars, the hunted otters, the massacred musk-oxen, the elephants slain by poachers' spears or by hunters' bullets, the starved calves, the beaten dogs, the blinded bears, the myxomatosis-harried rabbits, and the tormented bulls.

If so, may they be more merciful to us than we have been to them. And the most devastating thought of all is that they probably would be.

Appendix

Modern Breeds

European and American

From being originally all-purpose, cattle have become specialised. During the all-purpose era cattle provided milk, cream (for butter and cheese), meat, draught animals and bulls for sport. In considering modern commercial breeds we may eliminate draught oxen and fighting bulls, which leaves three main functions for twentieth-century cattle.

The breeds of the western world are generally divided into three categories, namely (a) beef; (b) dairy; and (c) dual-purpose.

Some breeds, notably the South Devon and the Race Normand, can reasonably claim to be triple-purpose, for their milk is particularly rich in butterfat and therefore excellent for making butter and cheese.

The following is a selection of the leading breeds in these categories.

ABERDEEN-ANGUS

Beef. Based on the traditional polled cattle of north-eastern Scotland, the Aberdeen-Angus was developed in the first half of the nineteenth century. Exports to North America began in 1873, the three bulls involved siring 800 calves in three years. The breed is now immensely strong in the United States and Canada. Most of the beef cattle in New Zealand are Aberdeen-Angus. There are also many herds in Argentina, South Africa, Australia and Chile, and recently there have been exports to China and Russia.

The breed has changed considerably from the early days, when it produced massive beef animals which took three or four years to mature. Now it is a short-legged, well-rounded beast, notable not only for the quality of its meat but for its ability to gain weight quickly. The best young bulls put on over a kilogram per day on a good diet.

Although black is now the official Aberdeen-Angus colour, red animals occur from time to time, and some of these have been used to introduce the polled factor in certain red breeds such as the Lincoln Red.

AYRSHIRE

Dairy. As noted on page 102, the Ayrshire breed was developed from a type of dairy cow long resident in Ayrshire and, even before the improvers took it in hand, highly regarded for its milk. Dutch imports, however, played an important part in its ancestry.

Ayrshire cows have a unique conformation, with very deep hindquarters and their udders tucked up well between their legs, so that the front quarter of the udder and the underside of the belly form more or less a straight line – not pendulous as in so many other breeds. They naturally have prominent, up-curving, lyre-shaped horns, but as most cattle are now dehorned these are seldom seen. The Ayrshire colours are brown (ranging from light reddish-brown to deep chocolate) and white. A polled strain of Ayrshires has been developed in U.S.A. and some have been sent to Britain.

Ayrshires have been exported to most countries of the world, and many of these have evolved their own Ayrshire types. Besides the newer countries, such as the United States, Australia and Canada, they are strong in Finland, Russia, and many countries in South America and Africa.

The bull is a formidable animal, bearing a distinct resemblance to pictures of the ancient aurochs. Apart from their more horizontal horns, the cattle of 3,000 B.C., depicted in the rock paintings of Jabbaren, in the Sahara, could well pass for Ayrshires.

BARZONA

Beef. A new breed created in Arizona from Afrikander, Angus, Hereford and Santa Gertrudis cattle, the idea being to breed an animal which would thrive on the sparse vegetation of the hot, dry Arizona countryside. The name is a combination of Arizona and Bard, a family owning extensive ranches in that area. The herd formed on the Bard ranch was closed in 1960, and a breed association was formed in 1968. The bulls are being used for crossing with Herefords. Colour – red.

BEEFMASTER

Beef. An American breed, the Beefmaster was developed in the 1930s by the Lasater family in Texas and Colorado, using Herefords, Shorthorns and zebus, with zebus probably predominant, though the exact proportions of each breed are not known. The breed is large, bulls weighing up to 2,600 lb., and very hardy. Colour – red.

BELTED GALLOWAY

Dual-purpose, though with an emphasis on beef. The Belted Galloway is a pied animal,

(Right above) *Blonde D'Aquitaine, "Jackaroo" a two-year-old.*
(Right below) *South Devon bull.*

144

mainly black but with a white belt which looks like a white sheet thrown over the central section of its body. This is a very ancient coloration pattern, found in a number of primitive types of cattle as well as in certain other species of animal, notably the tapir, and, by breaking up the body outline, is useful camouflage. Probably the basic stock from which the breed evolved was much the same as that of the Galloway, but, while the Galloway has concentrated on beef production, the Belted Galloway also produces some useful milkers. Overseas there are belted cattle in U.S.A., probably owing more to the Dutch Lakenvelder than to the Scottish Beltie, though there have been recent exports to the United States.

Belted Galloway bulls are very prepotent. The white belt which is their trademark persists in their offspring for many generations. It seems reasonable to suppose that other qualities, such as robust health and stamina, are likewise inherited by their progeny.

BLONDE D'AQUITAINE

Beef. A very large breed of south-western France, recently come into prominence in Britain and elsewhere as a crossing bull for producing beef from dairy cattle. It resembles the Charolais in size and appearance and has a similar growth rate. The importations to Britain, which began in 1972 and to the end of 1976 totalled 29 bulls and 346 heifers, were made with a view to reducing the proportion of difficult calvings, which sometimes result from the use of the Charolais.

Overseas, Blonde d'Aquitaine cattle have been introduced to U.S.A., Canada and New Zealand.

BRAFORD

Beef. A Brahman-Hereford cross, developed in the United States. A number of attempts have been made to produce a good, beef-producing animal using these two breeds, but the Braford breed as now established, with approximately three-eighths Brahman and five-eighths Hereford blood, was developed in Florida, on the Alto Adams Ranch. The Hereford influence is obvious, in the general red colour and the white (though red-marked) faces, but the general conformation is less compact, and the legs are longer. Also the horns are spreading, longer than in the Hereford and, in the cows, upward curved into sharp points. The breed is heat tolerant and thrives in the Florida climate. Bulls weigh up to 1,800 lb.

BRAHMAN (AMERICAN)

Beef. The American Brahman is really another name for the zebu, the first specimens of

(Left above) *Aberdeen-Angus bull, "Palernest of Haymount", sold for 10,000 guineas in 1973.*
(Left below) *Belted Galloway bull.*

which were exported from India to America in 1849. The name is probably derived from the sacred Brahmini bulls of ancient India.

The numbers involved in the nineteenth-century importations of Brahmans to the United States were small, and the animals were intended primarily for draught work in the southern states, but breeders were impressed by the quality of the progeny of these Brahman bulls on Shorthorn heifers. From 1924 onwards more Brahman bulls were brought in from Brazil, where the breed had become established as a result of large importations from India. Thereafter the Brahman stock in America rapidly increased, partly through the breeding of pure-bred animals and partly through the grading-up of cross-breds by an extensive use of Brahman bulls.

There are today enormous numbers of Brahman and Brahman-cross cattle in the United States, many of them on the ranges.

BRANGUS

Beef. An American breed developed to produce a beef breed for a subtropical climate. Its composition is five-eighths Angus and three-eighths Brahman. Unlike a number of the new American breeds, which were established by a single breeder and then closed their herd-books, the Brangus was developed simultaneously in several southern states, and new breeders can come in if they follow the same breeding programme. Colour – black. Horns – none; the breed is polled. Bulls weigh up to 2,000 lb, sometimes rather more. The breed has only a slight hump from its Brahman ancestry but has a pronounced dewlap. It is now well established in many Latin-American countries as well as in the southern United States.

The International Brangus Breeders' Association, however, decided not to accept the red colour, so the *Red Brangus* was developed as a separate breed. The Red Brangus, too, does not insist on the exact proportion of five-eighths Angus to three-eighths Brahman which is compulsory for all Brangus animals.

BRITISH WHITE

Dual-purpose. The British White is, in effect, a polled and domesticated version of the wild white cattle of which the Chillingham herd is an example. Its colour is white with black points – on ears, muzzle, points of horns and hooves, with sometimes flecks on legs and body.

Commercially, the performance of the British White is about on a par with an average Dairy Shorthorn. The breed has an extremely good bill of health and probably carries useful genes of resistance to disease. It has undeservedly become rare but is kept alive by a group of enthusiasts.

There is a small self-contained herd on the King Ranch, Texas, the descendants of a group sent to the U.S.A. during the Second World War to safeguard the herd from possible extinction.

146

BROWN SWISS

Dual-purpose. One of the most popular breeds in central Europe, where it originated in Alpine valleys in Switzerland and Austria, the Brown Swiss has also spread to the Americas, where it features prominently in the cattle population of the United States and Canada. In Illinois and neighbouring states in the Midwest, Brown Swiss are one of the major breeds in dairy herd. Its beefing potential is also quite good, and the butterfat content of the milk averages around 4%. Recently there has been interest in introducing the breed to Britain, as a meat producer. The Brown Swiss is one of the largest dairy breeds, its mature bulls usually weighing more than a ton. The colour is brown, though of varying shades, some almost grey; the horns are short and forward-curved. The breed is hardy and long-lived.

CANADIAN

Dual-purpose, though predominantly dairy. This is the indigenous breed of eastern Canada, centred on Quebec, and is descended from cattle introduced from northern France in the seventeenth century, the ancestors of the present Normandy breed and related to the Guernsey and Jersey. Over the centuries the breed has become very hardy and economical. There has been much inter-breeding with Ayrshires and latterly with Brown Swiss, but numbers of the old breed still exist. Colour – brown in cows, black in bulls.

CATTALO

Beef. This is the name given to crosses between the American bison (buffalo) and domestic cattle. Such crosses have been made since the early days of prairie settlement but with only qualified success. The first crosses were usually sterile – invariably so in the male, generally so in the female. Some breeders have persevered, particularly with Hereford crosses, and the work still goes on, though the incidence of fertile progeny is still low. Cattalo bulls look very like bison, though they are rather smaller.

CHAROLAIS

Beef. From their home in central and southern France Charolais cattle were introduced to Britain in the 1960s and quickly established a reputation as a major beef breed. The Herd Book of the British Charolais Cattle Society now has registrations of about 1,500 bulls and 1,500 heifers each year, but the impact on the British cattle population is even greater, owing to the extensive use of artificial insemination. The purpose behind the original importations was to produce fleshy, quick-maturing beef animals from dairy herds, particularly of Friesians, and in this the scheme has been successful, but many Charolais are now bred for their own sake. Crossbred Charolais cattle are now a common feature of the countryside. They range in colour from a

147

golden-fawn with white patches to mushroom brown and a fulvous grey and are in general large, upstanding animals.

Overseas, Charolais and Charolais crosses are well-established in the U.S.A., Canada, Mexico, New Zealand, Australia, Brazil and other countries. In America the Charolais/Brahman cross has resulted in the popular *Charbray*.

CHIANINA

Beef. One of the largest and oldest of Italian breeds, the white Chianina has its origins in the west central provinces of Italy, where it was traditionally used for both beef and draught purposes. A slight hump may indicate possible admixture of zebu blood.

This is one of the breeds introduced to Britain in the 1970s to produce beef from surplus calves from predominantly Friesian herds.

The Chianina is a huge animal, one of the largest of all breeds. Mature bulls stand more than 6 feet at the shoulders and weigh up to 4,000 lb. The breed is docile and easily handled, having originally been bred largely for draught work.

Chianinas have also been exported to the U.S.A., Canada, New Zealand, Brazil, Argentina, Uruguay and Mozambique.

CRIOLLO

Various purposes. Criollo is the name given to the descendants of the Spanish cattle exported centuries ago to the Latin American countries. For hundreds of years they were exposed to little but natural selection, with the result that they became hardy and well adapted to the climatic, disease and other stresses of the tropics and sub-tropics. In some areas milking types gradually evolved; in others the emphasis was on beef; in others they were mainly working animals. Besides these regional types, there have been programmes to improve the basic stock by crossing with other breeds, and these crossbreds now considerably outnumber the original Criollo types.

Examples are the *Cuban Criollo*, which has been developed as a dual-purpose breed, though, in this instance, with very little admixture of any other breed. Cows giving 1,200 or 1,300 gallons of milk per lactation have been recorded, and the mature bulls weigh up to a ton. Colour – golden brown, of various shades; horns – widespread and horizontal in the bull, up-curving in the cow.

The *Hispaniola Criollo*, which is found on the island of Hispaniola, comprising the republics of Santo Domingo and Haiti, is much smaller than the Cuban type, the mature bulls normally weighing less than half-a-ton. Colour – tan, as with the Cuban type; horns – rather longer and upswept.

The *Milking Criollo* is found mainly in Colombia and the neighbouring republics and in Central America. It is not a high yielder and is normally milked only once a day, but it thrives in a wide range of climates and is resistant to most diseases and parasites. Colour – yellow to dark red; horns – curving forwards and upwards.

The *Polled Criollo* is a beef-type animal, found in the northern lowlands of Colombia.

Charolais bull.

The poll is probably derived from a cross with either the Red Poll or the Angus. Colour – red.

The *Black-eared Criollo*, another Colombian type, though from the mountain regions, resembles very closely the British White, having black speckles and black ears. Why this resemblance should occur is not known. The breed is dual-purpose and very hardy. Unlike the British White, most animals are horned, though not all.

DAIRY SHORTHORN

Dual-purpose. As described on page 105, the Shorthorn type of cattle, widespread throughout England, Wales and lowland Scotland, was taken in hand by the Colling brothers in the second half of the eighteenth century. Their scientific breeding methods, on the lines of those employed by Bakewell, were devoted to producing good beef animals. In doing so they sacrificed much of the milking capacity for which the old type of Shorthorn was noted, and measures to restore it were taken by a younger contemporary of the Collings, Thomas Bates, of Kirklevington. As a result, the Shorthorns developed as two separate breeds, the Shorthorn (or *Beef Shorthorn*) and the Dairy Shorthorn.

However, the demarcation line between them was not clear. While the beef and the dairy types were kept pure at pedigree level, in the vast non-pedigree world, in which animals of Shorthorn type were strongly predominant, there was much indiscriminate cross-breeding. In the markets of nineteenth- and early twentieth-century England farmers showed a strong preference for handsome roan cattle, but there was nothing to indicate whether the animal they fancied would turn out to be a good milker or fit only for beef. Consequently, when the Friesians and Ayrshires offered reliable milkers they soon began to supersede the Dairy Shorthorns. Now that Friesians have largely taken the place of Dairy Shorthorns in the British milking herd, the surviving Dairy Short-horns, being the best, are much more reliable and consistent. They have excellent dual-purpose qualities.

In America the breed is known as the *Milking Shorthorn*.

DANISH RED

Dual-purpose. On the basis of the solids content of the milk, the Danish Red, or Red Dane, is the heaviest milking breed in Europe. It is the breed on which Danish butter production is founded. In recent years importations have been made to Britain to boost milk and butterfat production in the Dairy Shorthorn and Red Poll breeds, the latter of which it closely resembles. Up to about 1958 small importations of Danish Reds, or Red Danish as they were there known, were made to the U.S.A., but their early promise was spoiled by certain genetical defects which occurred in second-cross progeny, with the result that the breed is now rare in America.

DE LIDIA

This is the breed which produces the fighting bulls of Mexico. Breeding selection is for aggressiveness, which is meticulously tested at intervals from the time the cattle are a year old. The cattle are, however, the descendants of fighting animals imported from Spain in the seventeenth century. They are medium to small, with massive fore-quarters. Colour – black or deep grey; horns – wide, forward-curved and sharp. The bulls when mature weigh up to 1,200 lb. They are alert and move fast. Experts consider, however, that as fighting animals they are inferior to those of Spain.

DEVON

Beef. There have been red cattle in Devon from time immemorial. Doubtless in early times they were all-purpose cattle. As noted on page 108, during the Napoleonic Wars a strong demand for them in other parts of England led to a depletion of the best herds. Realizing the danger, Mr. Francis Quartly, of Molland, Devon, took the precaution of buying up the best stock offered for sale, thus laying the foundations of a great herd from which the modern Devon has evolved.

Early agricultural writers spoke of the Red Devon as a superb draught animal, a pair being capable of ploughing an acre of stiff land a day. Such a commendation would be of no value today, but the Devon has become an excellent producer of high-quality beef. It is short-legged, compact and very hardy. Overseas it is popular in semi-tropical countries, such as South Africa, Brazil and Australia. It is a good ranch breed.

DEXTER

Dual-purpose. The little Dexter is usually kept as a house-cow on small estates or small farms. The smallest British breed, the cow averages only about 650 lb in weight. The breed originated in Ireland, where it lived in the mountain districts of the south-west, working hard for its living in a wild, wet climate. Consequently it is an economic feeder, producing 500 to 600 gallons of milk a year for a very reasonable input of food, and its health record is good. Dexters have been exported to many parts of the world, in every continent and have adapted themselves satisfactorily.

The breed is kept dwarf by consistent selection, individuals which show signs of favouring the longer-legged Kerries, from which the Dexters developed, being eliminated. But the dwarfing gene is unfortunately associated with another which from time to time produces a deformity known as "bulldog calf". The calf, which always dies, has a flattened muzzle, like a bulldog. Happily, the condition is not very common.

DROUGHTMASTER

Beef. A new Australian breed, developed in Queensland from a mixed zebu and European breed ancestry. The zebu contribution was supplied chiefly by imported Brahman cattle from U.S.A., with some Santa Gertrudis; the European breeds involved were the Hereford, Devon, Shorthorn and Red Poll. Droughtmasters are big, deep-bodied animals, well adapted to life in tropical and sub-tropical climates. Colour – red. Some are horned, some polled.

FRIESIAN

Dairy, but tending towards dual-purpose. Today the Friesian is easily the most numerous breed in Britain, and probably Friesians in general are the most numerous dairy breed in the whole world. This position they owe to their unrivalled ability to produce large quantities of milk. Cows giving 2,000 gallons of milk per lactation are quite common; there are many records of 3,000-galloners; all the records for milk yields in the *Guinness Book of Records* were established by Friesian cows, the highest figure for a single lactation (365 days) being 4,508 gallons.

The Friesian, as its name indicates, originated in the Netherlands, from which it spread to many parts of western Europe. Most British dairy breeds probably owe something to Friesian blood introduced in the eighteenth and nineteenth centuries and perhaps earlier. The British Friesian, however, became a recognized British breed only in 1909, when the British Friesian Cattle Society was formed.

Friesian cattle (or, as they are called in the Americas, *Holstein*) are also plentiful in

Droughtmaster cattle at Greenmount Stud, Walkerstown, near Mackay, Queensland.

U.S.A., Canada, South Africa and many other countries the world over.

In recent years there has been a trend towards mating Friesian cows with large beef-type bulls, notably Charolais, to produce good beef calves. But the Friesian bulls themselves are huge animals, and surplus pure-Friesian calves make satisfactory beef when programme-fed without a check in yards. (See also *RED-AND-WHITE FRIESIAN.*)

GALLOWAY

Beef. Directly descended from cattle that have lived in Galloway, the south-west quarter of Scotland, from very early times, the Galloway owes less to admixture with other types than do most modern breeds. For a long time it had a reputation for being extremely hardy but slow-maturing, but careful selection coupled with a nutritious diet have speeded up its growth rate, and it can now compare with most other breeds.

The breed's chief colour is black, though dun and a shade of silvery dun have become popular with estate-owners in England. The coat is long, rough and readily curled. The breed is polled and has a kind of shaggy topknot, in contrast to the Aberdeen-Angus, whose skull rises to a point or peak at the crown.

Galloways have been exported to a number of countries but seem to have done best in South Africa. There have been recent exports to France and Italy.

152

GELBVIEH

Dual-purpose. This breed originating in northern Bavaria derives its name, Gelbvieh, meaning "yellow cattle", from its golden-yellow coat, like that of the Guernsey. It is similar in size and performance to the more numerous Simmental. A few have recently been imported into Britain and U.S.A., with a view to establishing its beef potential.

GUERNSEY

Dairy. The Guernsey, a splendid milk-producing cow, originates, of course, in the island from which it gets its name. Guernsey regulations regarding the importation of cattle into the island were not as strict or applied so early as in Jersey, and so the Guernsey cow is markedly different from the Jersey and owes more to outside influence.

Guernsey cows are golden yellow in colour, with some white markings, and have forward-curved horns, very like those of the Dairy Shorthorn. They are exceptionally docile – a characteristic which, however, does not always extend to the bulls (see opposite page 160). They are fine-boned and feminine in appearance, those now resident on the island being rather more so than the English type. Their milk is exceptionally rich and creamy, ideal for making butter, and some cows give high yields – 2,000 gallons or more per lactation.

Guernsey cattle have found their way to almost every country. They are well established in the United States, Australia, New Zealand, Canada, Kenya, India and wherever quality milk is appreciated. I believe I am correct in saying that the first calf ever to be born on the Antarctic continent was a Guernsey bull calf, whose dam was a cow which accompanied Admiral Byrd on his expedition in the 1930s. A polled strain has been developed in the U.S.A., and some animals have been shipped to Britain.

HAYS CONVERTER

Beef. A new breed developed in Canada by Senator Harry Hays, of Calgary, breeding for size, meat and quick growth rate. His basic stock were Herefords, Holsteins (animals specially selected for their good meat conformation, though without neglecting milk production) and Brown Swiss. The target of a bull weighing 3,000 lb., a cow weighing 2,000 lb. and a steer capable of achieving a 1,100 lb. carcase at twelve months, was in due course achieved. Colour – immaterial, though almost all have the white face of the Hereford and most are otherwise black. The breed is as yet small in numbers.

HEREFORD

Beef. In most of the great beef-producing countries of the world the white-faced Hereford is dominant. Immense herds populate the ranches of the United States, Canada, Australia, South America and dozens of other countries, from the tropics to the Arctic. It adapts itself admirably to range conditions, covering long distances in search of food and water and thriving on poor grazing, and yet it fattens readily when moved to fattening yards.

The breed originated in Herefordshire and other counties on the borders of England and Wales. Originally it had several colours, with red predominating, and the white face is said to have been introduced from Holland. On page 106 is an account of how this became established as a trade-mark of the Hereford breed. Now every Hereford and cross-bred Hereford wears it, and indeed a white face on any crossbred calf in a market is proof of Hereford blood in its ancestry and hence of its beef-producing potential. Most Herefords are now dehorned, and there are also two polled strains of Herefords in which the poll factor has been established genetically. (See *POLL HEREFORD*).

Both cows and bulls are exceptionally docile.

HIGHLAND

Beef. Highland cattle are exceptionally hardy, having had centuries, perhaps millenia, to adapt themselves to the cool, wet climate of the Scottish Highlands. There is something primitive about their shaggy, rough appearance and their enormous "handle-bar" horns. One senses that here is a direct descendant of the aurochs. There is a temptation to conclude that they have been little altered from time immemorial, but in the eighteenth and early nineteenth centuries, when great numbers found their way to English markets, where they were known as "Kyloes", they show a wider variation of type than they now possess. A picture in the Rothamsted collection of a West Highland Kyloe heifer of 1823 shows a fat, short-legged, piebald animal not a bit like the modern Highlander. Evidently the present-day Highlanders, which are golden-brown, dun, reddish-brown or brindled, are the result of deliberate selection (see opposite page 112).

On their native hills Highland cattle are required to search for their own living with a minimum of attention and to rear their own calves. This they do with perfect efficiency, but they need time to put on flesh. A Shorthorn bull on a Highland cow can, however, produce a fine, quick-maturing calf. Overseas, Highland cattle have been successfully introduced to many northern countries, including Russia, Canada and Sweden, and there are many of them in the windswept Falkland Islands.

In spite of their formidable appearance, Highland bulls are very docile.

JAMAICA HOPE

Dairy. The Jamaica Hope was registered as a distinct breed in 1952. It represents the results of years of experiment to find a type of cow which would produce good quantities of rich milk under tropical conditions, grazing largely on *Pangola* pastures. The chief contributors to the breed are the Jersey and the Sahiwal. Female Jamaica Hopes look very like Jerseys, though rather larger and deeper-bodied. Some of the males clearly show their Sahiwal (zebu) ancestry in the massive forequarters, the distinct hump and the forward-pointing horns. Milk production is reasonable. There are some 2,000-gallon cows, though the average is about 900, and the milk has a high butterfat content. As elsewhere, the demand in Jamaica is for large quantities of milk per cow, which favours the Holstein (Friesian) at the expense of the Jamaica Hope. Nevertheless, there are said to be now more than 50 herds in Jamaica, and cattle have been exported to a number of other countries in the West Indies and Central and South America.

JERSEY

Dairy. Small, dainty, lively, the Jersey is a specialist in the production of milk rich in butterfat. The average butterfat content of Jersey milk is over 5%, and records of more than 6% are not uncommon. Notes on the origin of the Jersey breed are found on page 101, where the fact is mentioned that no cattle have been imported into the island of Jersey since 1763. The big brown eyes, "dished" face, light build and general appearance have led to the legend that Jersey cattle have resulted from a cross between a cow and a deer. That is not so, but the breed, particularly the bulls, exhibits recognizable affinities with primitive types, notably the aurochs. Among the Jersey's other valuable characteristics are early maturity (the heifers are ready to start breeding at two years) and longevity. In spite of their somewhat fragile appearance, Jerseys are extremely hardy, and at one time (perhaps still) the northernmost milking herd in the world was of Jerseys (in Alaska). Elsewhere, Jerseys have colonized virtually every country.

Jersey bull, "Placid Dream Count".

Unlike bulls of many of the beef breeds, Jersey bulls are by no means docile. In general they are vigorous, virile, bad-tempered and difficult to handle.

KERRY

Dairy. This small black breed from south-western Ireland is not well known away from its native hills. Its small size, similar to that of the Jersey, may be due to the poor living to which the breed has become accustomed, for when taken to richer pastures in England and France it has shown a surprising capacity to increase both weight and milk yield. However, it has lagged behind in the improvement stakes and has received little attention.

Evidently descended from primitive types of black cattle that once roamed western Europe, the Kerry has most of the characteristics of indigenous and unimproved animals. It is hardy, long-lived and economical to feed.

LIMOUSIN

Beef. The Limousin belongs to the hilly regions of central France, where it runs in beef-suckler herds. It is not one of the largest and heaviest of breeds but produces good beef cattle of the right conformation and quick growth rate. The breed is hardy, outwintering satisfactorily. As a crossing breed it has produced good results when the bulls have been mated with Friesian cows, but when they have served Friesian heifers the problem of difficult calving has not been entirely overcome. The records of individual bulls are being investigated in an attempt to reduce the hazard.

A few Limousin cattle were introduced to Britain in 1971. A British Limousin Cattle Society has been formed and possesses a herd of its own. The breed has been exported to the U.S.A., Canada, New Zealand, South Africa, several South American countries, Spain, Portugal, Russia, Sweden and Madagascar, among other countries, and is becoming plentiful in America.

LINCOLN RED

Beef. Its full name is the Lincoln Red Shorthorn, and the breed originated simply as a local race of the Shorthorn. Early in the nineteenth century red Shorthorns were purchased at some of Collings' sales and taken to Lincolnshire. There, by consistent selection of red animals, they eventually became established as a separate breed.

For a long time there were two types of Lincoln Red, a dairy type and a beef type, each with a separate section in the Society's Herd Book, but of late years the emphasis has been almost entirely on beef. The Lincoln Red is, in general, larger and stands higher than the other two major red breeds, the Devon and the Sussex, but its chief recommendation is its ability to put on weight quickly. It is claimed to be the quickest maturing breed of all, and its bulls are much in demand for crossing with heifers of

"Filou", a Limousin bull born in 1970. He has been widely used as a sire for offspring exported to U.S.A.

other breeds. Overseas it has been most successful in sub-tropical lands, such as Brazil, South Africa and Chile, and there are now well-established breed societies in Canada, Australia and New Zealand.

LONGHORN

Beef. This was the breed on which Robert Bakewell worked and about which many details will be found from page 95 to page 105. After Bakewell's time interest in the breed waned, perhaps largely because Bakewell's insistence on enhancing the beef qualities of the breed sacrificed some of its other characteristics. The Longhorn was admirably adapted to fattening on the rich pastures of the Midlands, but it took its time over the process. Also many breeders, of Bakewell's time and subsequently, tended to regard it primarily as a draught ox. Interest was revived late in the nineteenth century, and a breed society formed in 1899. The general decline was not really arrested until recently, but the breed is now safe from extinction and is at last increasing in numbers.

In spite of its formidable appearance, the Longhorn bull is docile.

LUING

Beef. The Luing (pronounced "Ling") breed has been created in the present century by the Cadzow brothers on the island of Luing, in the Hebrides, using Beef Shorthorns and Highlanders as their basic stock. The cattle are bred to thrive in the exposed, windy coastal regions of western Scotland and are in consequence very hardy. They are compact, deep-bodied animals, not particularly large but producing a high proportion of the best quality meat. The herds are run as beef sucklers, and the cows are superlative mothers.

Luing colours are red, yellowish-red, yellow and white, with many roans. An export trade has already been developed, in live cattle and semen, to the U.S.A., Canada and New Zealand.

MAINE-ANJOU

Dual-purpose. A large, heavy animal, not unlike a big Dairy Shorthorn, the Maine-Anjou originated in the old French provinces of Maine and Anjou and those farther east. It owes something to an infusion of Shorthorn blood in the mid-nineteenth century. In the 1970s small numbers have been introduced to Britain with a view to examining their beef potential.

The colours are red and white; the horns are as in the Dairy Shorthorn. Maine-Anjou cattle have been exported to the U.S.A. and Canada and are becoming popular in both countries.

MARCHIGIANA

Beef and draught. A general-purpose breed originating in the region of Ancona, on the Adriatic coast of Italy. With the disappearance of a demand for working oxen, the Marchigiana has specialized in beef production and is now one of the most widespread breeds in Italy. It is a tall, white breed, with some zebu traits, including a well-developed dewlap. Nine bulls and 191 heifers were exported to Britain in 1974 for trial purposes. Although large, the cross-bred progeny of a Marchigiana bull on dairy cows is said to produce very few calving difficulties, chiefly because the calves at birth are very slim (see opposite page 160).

The breed is becoming popular in South America.

MAREMMA

Draught and beef. Maremma cattle are in all probability a very ancient breed, domiciled in central and southern Italy, where they graze free-range on pastures and marshland. The adult bulls are massive animals, weighing up to a ton and showing certain resemblances to the aurochs bulls. There seems also to be a trace of zebu blood in their ancestry, demonstrated by the deep dewlap. The horns are wide and up-curved, of medium length though sharp-pointed in the cows, but long and powerful in the bulls. The colour is greyish-white, darker in the bulls. In Italy Maremma cattle (cows and steers) are employed for draught purposes.

158

MEUSE-RHINE-IJSSEL

Dual-purpose. Now that this breed is becoming quite well known in Britain it is commonly referred to as MRI. Its ancestry is the same as that of the Friesian (the rivers in its name indicating its homeland), but it has developed as a separate red-and-white breed. In the late 1960s MRI cattle were imported into Britain with a view to reinforcing the Dairy Shorthorn breed, a programme which is still continuing. Subsequently interest has been shown in its performance as a beef breed, mature bulls weighing up to 2,900 lb. A Meuse-Rhine-Ijssel Cattle Society has been formed.

Overseas, it has been exported to the U.S.A. and Canada. In the U.S.A., as in Britain, the breed has been used for improving the milk yields of the Milking (Dairy) Shorthorn, but apparently no distinction is made between the Meuse-Rhine-Ijssel and the Red-and-White Friesian (Holstein).

MURRAY GREY

Beef. The Murray Grey is an outstanding beef breed created in Australia in 1905 by the Sutherland family, using as basic stock Aberdeen-Angus bulls and light roan Shorthorn cows. It is a polled breed, with a long, well-proportioned body and short legs. The colours range from dark grey to chocolate but with a sleek silver-grey predominating. The cows calve easily and milk well. The young stock grow rapidly, are efficient converters of grass to beef, and produce carcases with a high yield of edible meat. The breed is docile and placid. Murray Grey bulls weigh up to 2,200 lb.

Murray Greys were introduced to Britain in 1973 and now have a British breed society, with, at the most recent count, 10 bulls and 78 females. Aberdeen-Angus females are also being graded up by the use of Murray Grey bulls in successive generations. Murray Greys have also found their way to the United States, Canada, New Zealand and China. They are highly adaptable to climate, in Australia being found from the humid tropics, through the temperate regions, to the edge of the deserts and the snows of the Australian Alps.

NORMANDE

Triple-purpose; it is excellent for both milk and meat and its milk has a high butterfat content. In France, where it is the predominant breed in most of the northern and north-western departments, there are about 6,000,000 cattle of the Race Normande, of which 2,600,000 are milking cows. Its milk production is consistent, though at lower levels than that of the Friesian. An average for 186,000 lactations was 3,503 kg of milk at 4.18% butterfat. Norman breeders maintain that the butterfat content never falls below 4%, which is important to them, with their long tradition of making high-quality butter and cheese, including some of the best-known gourmet cheeses, such as Camembert, Livarot and Pont l'Eveque.

For meat production, the chief characteristic of the Normande is a small frame on which flesh grows very quickly. The cow is a short-bodied, stocky animal, not unlike the best type of Dairy Shorthorn. In France, where much of the beef comes from culled cows, the ability of the Normande cow to produce a rounded, well-fleshed carcase after years of milking is important. And the breed *is* long-lived. It is quite usual to find cows of 13 or 14 years still in full milk production. The breed does not, however, specialize in old-cow beef.

The Normande breed is based on the original stock of north-western France, with probably some admixture of Scandinavian blood a 1,000 years ago. It was reinforced by importations of Shorthorn cattle from England for a short period from 1850. It experienced great improvements between 1850 and 1890, and the Herd Book was established in 1883. In 1973 a British Normande Cattle Society was formed, but the numbers in England are still few.

OLD GLOUCESTERSHIRE

Dual-purpose, though mainly dairy. It would not be unfair to describe the original Old Gloucestershires as dairy editions of the Longhorn. Their territory adjoined and overlapped, and their colour pattern was similar though not identical. Both Longhorns and Old Gloucestershires possess the distinct "finching" or white spinal stripe. The Old Gloucestershire's basic body colour is deep brown, in some instances almost black. In conformation the Old Gloucestershire resembles the Dairy Shorthorn, with short, forward-curving horns.

The breed was once the dominant dairy animal in the Severn vale, around Gloucester, and also across the border into Wales, where the now extinct Glamorgan type was very similar. Its milk was particularly suitable for making cheese and was the basic material for the celebrated Double Gloucester cheeses. The fact that it chose this speciality, which proved to have little future, was an element in its decline. Whatever the main cause, it dwindled to near-extinction, and by the 1950s only one fairly small herd and some scattered animals survived. Since then the breed has been saved and established on a satisfactory footing, though it is still low in numbers. It is a useful dual-purpose animal, without breaking any production records, and it is hardy, long-lived and docile.

PINZGAUER

All-purpose. The Pinzgauer is a primitive breed very similar to the Old Gloucestershire breed of England. It has the same chocolate brown colour, shading to black, with the

(Right above) *Guernsey bull.*
(Right below) *"Lupo", champion Marchigiana bull at the Macerata Show, Italy. He weighed 3000 lb at 4½ years and shows the long, well-muscled conformation much favoured in western countries.*

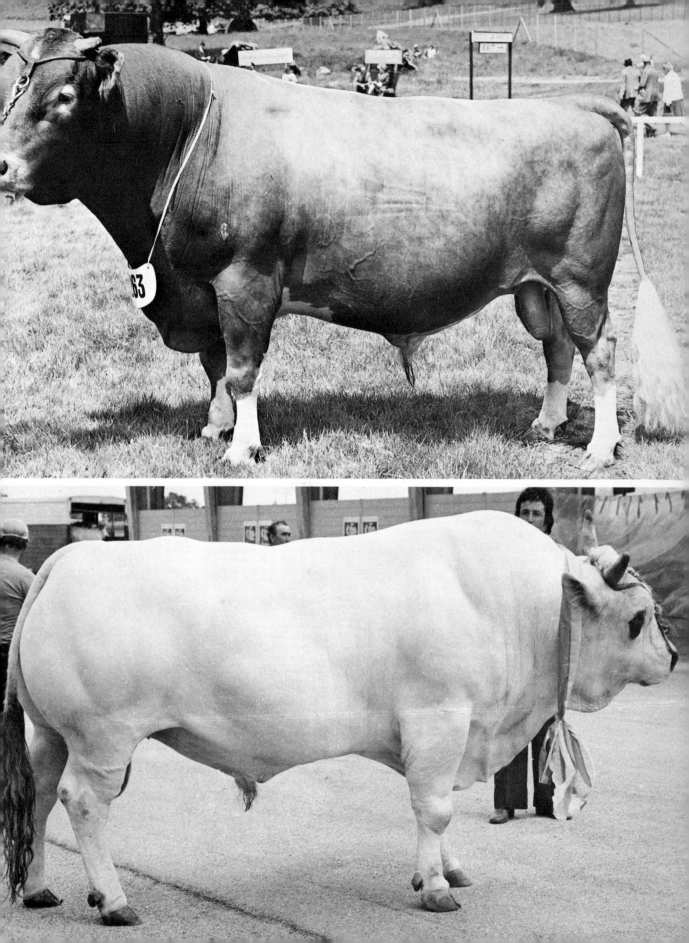

conspicuous white spinal stripe and tail, known as "finching". In the Pinzgauer there may be rather more white, especially on the flanks and belly.

The breed originated in the Pinzgau valley, amid the Austrian mountains, where it was required to serve all purposes. It had a reputation as a good draught animal. The cows are milked in their Austrian homeland, but the future of the breed is probably as a beef producer. A few Pinzgauer animals have been exported to Britain in 1976, and a British Pinzgauer Cattle Society has been formed.

POLL HEREFORDS

The development of Poll Herefords is an interesting story.

In 1901 an Iowa Hereford breeder, Warren Gammon, sent a circular letter to the 2,500 members of the American Hereford Cattle Breeders' Association to enquire whether any of them had in their herds the hornless "freaks" which were known to occur occasionally. Sifting replies, he eventually acquired 13 such animals – six males and seven females. From these foundation stock all the American Poll Herefords, a million or so of them, have sprung.

Uruguay, Argentina and Australia started similar schemes in the first decade of this century, their stock being increased subsequently by importations of poll animals from the U.S.A., Canada, South Africa and New Zealand followed suit, and at the beginning of World War II Poll Herefords were well established in these countries.

In Britain the process did not begin till after the war. In 1948 Lt.-Colonel D. Talbot Rice arranged for semen from a Poll Hereford bull in Mississippi to be flown via Canada to his herd at Fossbridge, near Cheltenham. Artificial insemination was then something of a novelty, and the deep freeze technique had not been developed. The consequence of delays was that only one calf resulted from the experiment, the famous bull "Coln Arthur". It attracted wide attention but unfortunately its dam proved to be a cow whose pedigree could not be traced, and so its contribution towards the building of a Poll Hereford strain in Britain was not as effective as it might have been.

Because of his doubtful pedigree, it was necessary to form a new Association for "Coln Arthur"'s progeny. As soon as this Association was thoroughly established breeders began to fortify it by new importations of polled stock from New Zealand, Canada, U.S.A. and Australia. Several hundreds of animals, all with fully authenticated pedigrees, were brought in. But their register had to be kept separate from the one in which the progeny of "Coln Arthur" was recorded, partly because of that lapse in the pedigree of his dam and partly because the Hereford Herd Book Society did not recognize calves bred by artificial insemination. So at that time there were three Hereford societies operating in Britain – one horned and two polled – though the Hereford Herd Book Society agreed to keep all the records.

(Left above) *Masai cattle on the plains of Kenya.*
(Left below) *A Zebu bull.*

While all this was going on, another group of breeders adopted another method of introducing the poll factor into the Hereford world. They selected one of the best Galloway bulls alive – "Ambassador of Knockarling" – and mated him with a selection of Hereford cows. The poll factor thus introduced, matings in succeeding generations were, of course, all with pure Herefords, and the Galloway blood was soon down to less than 1%.

Finally, in 1958 yet another scheme introduced the poll factor into a new group of Herefords by using a Red Angus bull on Hereford cows.

All the programmes were successful, and about a third of the Herefords now registered annually in Britain are polled.

RED-AND-WHITE FRIESIAN

Dual-purpose. In their Dutch homeland Friesian cattle were originally either black-and-white or red-and-white. The British Friesian Cattle Society has long frowned upon red-and-white individuals, which occasionally crop up in black-and-white herds. As these animals seemed to some breeders to be in no way inferior to their black-and-white herd-mates, a Red-and-White Friesian Cattle Society was formed to cater for them. There is now a considerable number of red-and-white herds, which in general match the performance of the conventional black-and-whites.

The prejudice against red-and-white Friesians in the Netherlands probably arose from the breed having the Meuse-Rhine-Ijssel breed, which are red-and-white, on the southern borders of its territory, so precautions were advisable to keep the breed pure. In America a Red-and-White Holstein Society has been founded, as in Britain, and there has been much crossing with other breeds of red, white or red-and-white cattle.

RED POLL

Dual-purpose. The chief ancestor of the Red Poll was the *Suffolk Dun*, now extinct but once dominant in the county which gave it its name. It was a dairy breed, noted for milk production and for the richness of its milk. Another major element in the breeding of the Red Poll was another extinct type, the *Norfolk*, which was a small, horned animal, said to be like "the Herefordshire breed in miniature". The two together have combined to produce the Red Poll, though probably with some outside help. In early times both parent breeds may have been derived, at least to some extent, from stock brought over from Denmark, and during the past two or three decades the Red Polls have been reinforced by infusions of the very similar Danish Red breed.

The Red Poll is short-legged, round-bodied and, of course, polled. Its performance both as a beef and a dairy animal is good without being brilliant. In the 1920s and 1930s Red Polls had an enviable record of major awards in milk and meat classes at the London shows, but since then they have given way in the dairy classes to the ubiquitous Friesians and in the beef lines to the specialist beef breeds. At the moment they are in eclipse but are by no means obsolescent. They fatten quickly and economically, and milking cows continue production through an impressive number of lactations. The bulls are very prepotent and have been used extensively for crossing, notably to introduce the polled factor into several horned breeds.

Overseas, the Red Poll has done well in Africa, West Indies, Australia and Central and South America. There is a flourishing Red Poll Cattle Club in the U.S.A., though the breed has declined in numbers in recent years.

ROMAGNOLA

Beef and draught. One of the more important Italian breeds, the Romagnola's original home is Tuscany and neighbouring provinces. It has upright horns and probably possesses some zebu blood. The colour is grey-white shading to dark grey on shoulders and tail, as in many zebu breeds. As the demand for oxen for draught work has tapered off, the Romagnola has been concentrating on its beef potential, which is considerable. 6 bulls and 200 heifers were exported to Britain in 1974 and a British Romagnola Cattle Society formed. The breed has also sent cattle to U.S.A. and Australasia.

SAHIWAL

Primarily dairy. This zebu breed, developed in the West Punjab, has now spread not only to much of the rest of India and Pakistan but to large regions of Africa and to some South American countries; also to the West Indies, Australia, the Philippines and the United States. The Sahiwal is a long, deep-bodied animal, the bulls standing up to 5 feet in height and weighing up to 1500 lb. They have prominent humps and dewlaps. The cows have a better capacity for milk production than have many Indian breeds, some recorded herds averaging 700 to 750 gallons per lactations, with some individuals producing over 1,000 gallons. The level of feeding undoubtedly has much to do with it. With such potentiality, the Sahiwal has proved an excellent breed to cross with European dairy breeds in the tropics, making as its main contribution resistance to tropical diseases and adaptation to life in hot climates.

Sahiwals are docile, lethargic animals, often considered too slow and sleepy for draught work. Their horns are short and curled, often non-existent. Red is the usual colour.

SANTA GERTRUDIS

Beef. The Santa Gertrudis is a breed deliberately created for use in hot climates. The world-famous King Ranch, of southern Texas, was its cradle. Having started their cattle-breeding venture with Texas Longhorns and having later introduced Short-horns, Herefords and Brahmans, the Kleberg family, owners of the Ranch, decided that the type of cattle which would best suit the conditions would be five-eighths Shorthorn and three-eighths Brahman.

In 1917/18 a group of crossbred Brahman-Shorthorn cows, among them the best milk cows on the Ranch, were mated with an outstanding Brahman bull. Among the progeny was a red bull named "Monkey", who proved such a remarkable sire that every Santa Gertrudis animal in the world is directly descended from him. The breed was officially recognized in 1940.

From its Shorthorn ancestry the Santa Gertrudis has inherited its early maturity, fine fleshing qualities and red colour. From the Brahman, its loose hide, short hair, much of its conformation, and its adaptability to life in hot climates. It makes good, economical use of grazing and can fatten on range, though in America most stock is fattened in feedlots.

The Santa Gertrudis is a big breed, service bulls averaging about 2,200 to 2,400 lb. in weight. Its colour is deep red, and the horns are rather short and droop downwards. From Texas the breed has spread to most states in the United States and to 30 or 40 other countries. The King Ranch itself has huge satellite ranches in Pennsylvania, Australia and Brazil, and, when I last visited it, had 42,000 breeding cows in Texas alone (though some of these were, I think, crossbreds). It is a tribute to the versatility of the Santa Gertrudis that it thrives equally well in Queensland, with a rainfall of 150 inches, to Texas, which is dusty and arid.

A polled strain has been developed in Texas.

SHORTHORN

Beef. Often known now as the *Beef Shorthorn*. Pages 105–6 give an account of the improvement of the Shorthorn breed by the Colling brothers and others. The beef qualities of the breed were fostered and exaggerated to produce the "Durham Ox" and even greater monstrosities. Thomas Bates's development of the Dairy Shorthorn was a corrective to that trend. Later the beef section of the breed settled down to a more reasonable programme and became a superb beef breed. Much credit for this later development is due to enlightened Scottish breeders, particularly in Aberdeenshire. As a result of their good work, the Shorthorn was ready to take a major part in the establishment of a beef industry in many countries overseas. In 1823 a Shorthorn bull, "Tarquin", exported to Buenos Aires, laid the foundations of the Argentine beef herds, in which there is still a great deal of Shorthorn blood. Large numbers of Shorthorns were also sent to the U.S.A., Canada, Australia and South Africa, and buyers return every year to buy first-class bulls at British shows and sales. In the middle years of the twentieth century there was a trend towards breeding a small, compact type of animal, attractive enough but rather too light; this is now being corrected (see page 167).

Beef Shorthorn bulls are extensively used for crossing, especially with Galloway and Highland cows. The Shorthorn-Galloway cross produces the blue-grey cattle very popular in northern markets.

Just as the Lincoln Red developed from an offshoot of the Shorthorn breed, so now the *Whitebred Shorthorn* is embarked on a similar career. It already has a Whitebred Shorthorn Association, which registers about 110 bulls and 120 heifers each year. The Whitebred Shorthorn exists really for one purpose only, to provide the male half of the cross with the Galloway which produces the very popular blue-grey cows, which are extensively used in beef-suckling herds.

There is a polled strain of Shorthorn in U.S.A., developed by crossing with a polled breed in the late nineteenth century. It has a separate promotion society, though its registrations are made by the American Shorthorn Breeders Association.

SIMMENTAL

Dual-purpose. One of the major cattle breeds on the continent of Europe, the Simmental originated in Switzerland but has now spread both westwards and eastwards, acquiring some variations in the process. The German *Fleckvieh* ("spotted cattle") and the French *Pie-Rouge de l'Est* ("pied red cattle of the East") are derived from them, and the yellow-and-white cattle I have seen in Hungary are obviously of the same type. Beginning in 1970 considerable importations of Simmental have been made to Britain, the total number of cattle involved being around 1700. Breeding is proceeding apace, and by August, 1975, 1553 British-bred bulls and 1464 heifers had been registered, to say nothing of many crossbreds in the process of up-grading.

Interest in Britain has been in the breed's beef-producing potential. The Simmental is not a huge beast but it grows fast and has a carcase yielding high proportions of quality meat. Simmental × Friesian calves have demonstrated in trials that they grow faster and produce better carcases than pure Friesians. But when mated with Friesian heifers the cross produces a higher proportion of difficult calvings than is acceptable, so it is recommended only with mature cows. Individual bulls are being monitored with a view to eradicating the problem.

The general Simmental colours are brown (or red) and white, the red ranging from a deep brown-red to fawny-yellow.

SOUTH DEVON

Dual-purpose. Indeed, the South Devon can be reckoned triple-purpose, for besides being an excellent beef and milk-producing animal, it gives milk very rich in butterfat and classified with Jersey and Guernsey milk for a special quality premium. It is the largest British breed – a huge, slab-sided animal which may stand six feet high at the withers. On the rich pastures of south Devon and east Cornwall, which are its home, it grows quickly and rapidly covers its big frame with flesh. Hardy and trouble-free, it is one of the most economical breeds for all purposes.

Its origins are unknown. Probably there was a basic stock similar to that from which the Red Devon was produced, but one suspects that there has been an admixture of Guernsey blood. Since the introduction of a number of French breeds to Britain during the 1960s and 1970s some of their crosses have produced animals not unlike the South Devon in appearance, which gives rise to the suspicion that similar imports, in the unrecorded past, perhaps of Charolais and Blonde d'Aquitaine, played a part in the development of the South Devon. The colour of the South Devon is golden brown; the horns are short or of moderate length and are curved forward (see opposite page 144).

Overseas, the South Devon has done well in South Africa, Australia, New Zealand, U.S.A, Brazil, Central America and a number of other countries. A problem arises from the fact that the breed is so small numerically that it cannot meet all the demands for exports (including those from other counties of England!), and obtaining good heifers is often difficult. The breed is good-tempered and docile.

SUSSEX

Beef. The Sussex breed were originally regarded as primarily draught animals, and the use of oxen for ploughing continued in Sussex longer than in any other part of England, with perhaps one exception. Now they have developed into a first-class beef breed, excelling in producing early-maturing steers and heifers. Many of them having been bred on the bleak levels of Romney Marsh and Pevensey, they are very hardy and need little attention. Their former propensity for pulling ploughs and carts has made them good movers and hence readily adaptable to life on extensive ranches, where they have to travel far to find their living. Their colour is deep red, almost purple; their horns horizontal or down-curved in the bulls, generally longer and up-curved in the cows, though some 15% are now polled.

Overseas, the Sussex has specialized in the South and East African market, where it has been highly successful. In particular, it has been used for crossing with Afrikander cattle.

A few Sussex have been introduced to America since the Second World War, most of them to Texas. A polled strain has been established through the agency of a Red Angus bull, and the U.S.A. has some of these.

TEXAS LONGHORN

Beef. The Longhorn of Texas and neighbouring states, both in the United States and in Mexico, is descended from long-horned cattle introduced by Spaniards. Over the centuries the breed adapted itself to life on the hot, dry ranges and became very numerous. When, in the 1870s, white settlement advanced quickly westwards over the American prairies, eliminating the bison as it advanced, the grass, with no bison to eat it, grew luxuriantly. Settlers looked around for cattle to graze it and found the Texas Longhorn ready to hand. For a time the entire mid-West, from Texas to Wyoming, was stocked largely with Longhorns, and America's great beef industry was founded on it.

Better breeds from a commercial viewpoint were, however, available and either replaced or were crossed with the Longhorns. In consequence, pure Longhorns became rare and were saved from extinction only by action by a few enlightened breeders and by the United States Government, who set aside reserves for them in Oklahoma and Nebraska. Now, with the realization that this unsophisticated, hardy breed carries

"Morphic Galaxy", *supreme champion at the Beef Shorthorn Cattle Show at Perth, Scotland,*
in 1973.

valuable genetic traits, American cattle-breeders appreciate the foresight of the con-
servationists. The genes of particular value are those for "high fertility, easy calving,
some disease and parasite resistance, hardiness, longevity and high browse and coarse
forage utilization on marginal range-lands".

Texas Longhorns are similar in many respects to the English Longhorn. The bulls
are massive and stand from five to six feet at the shoulders; their horns are wide and
straight, up-tilted at the end. The cows, which have rather long legs, are often
equipped with enormous, up-curving horns like handlebars. Colours are various
patterns, often complex, of brindle and white. As befits a breed adapted to searching for
a living in inhospitable country, the Longhorn moves fast and is alert and sprightly. It
matures slowly and its milk capacity is not great, but its progeny resulting from crosses
with such breeds as the Hereford, Shorthorn, Friesian and Charolais appear to be full of
promise.

WELSH BLACK

Dual-purpose. From about the middle of the twentieth century the Welsh Black breed
has made great strides and is now an excellent dual-purpose breed to be reckoned with,

167

"Dysyhni Boy", a Welsh Black bull, bred in Merionethshire, in 1970 and sold for export to New Zealand in 1973.

though with an emphasis on beef rather than milk. Before that it had tended to lag behind during the age of improvement. Black cattle were widespread in Wales from very early times, but in the course of centuries several types had developed. North Wales and Anglesey had cattle in which beef qualities were predominant. South-west Wales had a dairy strain, known as Castle-martins. There were also naturally polled Welsh cattle and, in parts of North Wales, a belted type, like the Belted Galloway in colour, which still survives in small numbers.

Now that the Welsh Black is concentrating on commercial qualities it is proving capable of producing quick-maturing beef beasts which can challenge most breeds on a basis of rate of weight gains. As might be expected from the nature of its native country, it is hardy, healthy and economical to feed. The colour is black; the bull's horns curve slightly downward, while the cow's are longer and sweep forward and upward.

Overseas, the Welsh Black has been exported to the U.S.A., India, Jamaica, New Zealand and several countries in South America and Africa. There is little doubt that it will invade other markets in the future.

African and Asian

The typical cattle of India and many other countries of East Asia are zebus, which have prominent humps and deep, pendulous dewlaps. Most breeds or types are larger than the domestic cattle of the West and have longer legs. They grunt rather than low or bellow, and are seldom or never to be seen standing knee-deep in water. Well adapted to life in a tropical climate, they seem indifferent to heat and seldom seek shade. The commonest colour is silvery grey, but some breeds are predominantly red and others have a proportion of red animals (amounting, in the Tharparkar breed of Pakistan, to 25%).

Zebus can be subdivided into several main types by the shape of their horns, as follows:

Lyre-shaped Horns. An example is the *Kankrej* which is probably the biggest of Indian zebus. Originating on the west coast of India they have now spread to much of the sub-continent and have also been exported to South American countries. They are reckoned to be a draught and milk breed, being too slow to mature at present for economical beef production. Indian breeders set great store on the magnificent horns, sometimes making then even larger by surgical manipulation.

Lateral Horns. The horns grow out laterally from the skull but then, in many instances, curve. Described as an all-purpose breed, the *Gir*, which is probably the most important of this group, is another west coast breed of India. It is docile and lethargic. Gir cattle have done well when exported to other countries, notably Brazil, and have played an important part in the development of the American Brahman.

Long Horns. There are a number of Indian breeds, among which two of the most notable are the *Hallikar* and *Amrit Mahal*. Both are considered good draught animals, largely because of their speed, agility and quick movements. The Amrit Mahal breed is said to have been developed by the rulers of Mysore for army transport. They were also used for racing, pulling light carts. The temperament of both breeds has been described as fiery.

Short Horns. Although, as with most Indian breeds, the breeds of this type are used for draught purposes in India most of them are considered to have useful milking

Brahmans (white) and Afrikanders grazing together in pastures at the National Cattle Breeding Station at Belmont, Rockhampton, Queensland.

potential. Examples of short-horned breeds are the *Bhagnari*, the *Hariana* and the *Ongole*. The last of these, originating on the east coast of India, north of Madras, has been extensively exported to Brazil and thence to the U.S.A., to play its part in the development of the American Brahman.

In addition, there are several rather small breeds of intermediate type, such as the *Kumauni*, the *Alambadi* and the *Lohani*, all of them used primarily for draught purposes though some have milking potential. Sri Lanka (Ceylon) has a small indigenous breed with short horns, the *Sinhala*. There is a breed of zebu-type in South China. The native cattle of Burma, Thailand, Indo-China and northern Malaya are intermediate between humped and humpless types, as is the *Chinese Yellow* breed.

Zebu-type cattle have spread to much of Africa, constituting a big proportion of the cattle population of the countries on the eastern side of the continent. Examples are the *Boran*, which graze in enormous numbers on the plains of Kenya and Ethiopia, the *Small East African Zebu*, the predominant type in much of East Africa, and the *Sudanese*. Father south, the place of the Small East African Zebu is taken by the rather similar *Angoni* in Malawi, Zambia and Mozambique. Madagascar has its own type of zebu. West Africa, too, has a number of zebu-type breeds in the savannah country south of the Sahara, the *Fulani* being especially widespread and numerous.

170

Besides these humped cattle, Africa has many intermediate types, probably resulting from crosses between humped and humpless breeds. They are particularly plentiful in the states of southern central Africa, where there has been considerable interbreeding with European breeds.

The humpless cattle of Africa are probably descended from wild cattle of the aurochs type which once roamed over much of northern Africa and are depicted in the rock paintings of the Sahara. Libya, Morocco and Algeria have indigenous humpless breeds, while south of the Sahara the *N'Dama* breed (also known as the *Red Senegal*) has a very wide distribution from Senegal to Nigeria.

One of the more important intermediate breeds, resulting from crosses between humped and humpless animals, is the *Afrikander*, a breed used by the Hottentots of South Africa when the first Europeans landed. Afrikanders are big animals, commonly weighing up to a ton and sometimes more. They are hardy, resistant to disease, mostly docile and with considerable beef potential. Some have been exported to Australia and Texas.

Another is the *Nguni*, found chiefly in the Transvaal. It is fairly small, not much more than half the size of the Afrikander and is considered useful for milking, especially when crossed with the Jersey or Friesian. It is noted for, among other characteristics, its extremely variable coloration, which covers most of the permutations of white, red, black, yellow, brown and dun. Some are spotted or flecked, producing a hide valuable for covering shields. Others are white with black ears, muzzle and eyelashes, much like the British Whites and the Chillingham cattle. A recognized type, known as *Inkone*, has a dark-coloured panel, often red, on the sides of the body, which, apart from that and a few red markings elsewhere on the hide, is otherwise white.

In Asia there are humpless breeds in Turkey and northern Iraq, notably the *Oksh*, and also in China. Intermediate types in south-east Asia are in some instances the result of crossing with wild cattle, including the *Banteng* (see page 22) and the *Gaur* (see page 20).

Bibliography

Boston, Eric J., *Jersey Cattle* (1954); Brand, John, *Observations on Popular Antiquities* (1900); Burton, Maurice, *Animals of Europe* (1973); Church, Leslie, *Knight of the Burning Heart* (1938); Cottrell, Leonard, *The Bull of Minos* (1955); Curwen E. Cecil, & Hatt, Gudmund, *Plough and Pasture* (1953); Deane, Tony, & Shaw, Tony, *The Folklore of Cornwall* (1975); Fraser, Allan, *Beef Cattle Husbandry* (1959), *Animal Husbandry Heresies* (1960), *Breeder & Boffin* (1962), *The Bull* (1972); Frazer, Sir James, *The Golden Bough* (Abridged Edition, 1922); Garrad, G. H., *A Survey of the Agriculture of Kent* (1954); Gurney, O. R., *The Hittites* (1952); Hagedoorn, A. L., *Animal Breeding* (ed. Allan Fraser, 1962); Hemingway, Ernest, *Death in the Afternoon* (1932); Jackman, E. R., & Long, R. A., *The Oregon Desert* (1964); Jenkins, Alan C., *Wild Life in Danger* (1970); Kelley, R. B., *Native and Adapted Cattle* (1959); Kerridge, Eric, *The Farmers of Old England* (1973); Lewis, C. S., *The Problem of Pain* (1957); Long, W. Harwood, *A Survey of the Agriculture of Yorkshire* (1970); Luce, J. V., *The End of Atlantis* (1969); Mannix, Daniel P., *Those About to Die* (1960); Marks, John, *To the Bullfight* (1952), *To the Bullfight Again* (1966); Meat & Livestock Commission, *British Beef Cattle* (1976); Milk Marketing Board, *Twenty-five Million* (1965); Orwin, C. S., *A History of English Farming* (1949); Palmer, Joan Austin, *From Plough to Porterhouse* (1966); Pawson, H. C., *A Survey of the Agriculture of Northumberland* (1961); Payne, Robert, *The Roman Triumph* (1962); Payne, W. J. A., *Cattle Production in the Tropics* (1970); Piggott, Stuart, *Prehistoric India* (1952); Porter, Enid, *Cambridgeshire Customs & Folklore* (1969); Powell, T. G. E., *The Celts* (1963); Readers' Digest Association, *The Living World of Animals* (1970), *The Last Two Million Years* (1973), *Folklore, Myths & Legends of Britain* (1973); Richthofen, Walter Baron von, *Cattle-Raising on the Plains of North America* (1885); Rouse, John, *World Cattle I, II & III* (1970, 1970 & 1973); Russell, Sir E. John, *English Farming* (1941); Seebohm, M. E., *The Evolution of the English Farm* (1952); Seshabri Balakrishna, *The Twilight of India's Wild Life* (1969); Spence, Lewis, *The History & Origins of Druidism*; Stuart, Lord David, *An Illustrated History of Belted Cattle* (1970); Symon, J. A., *Scottish Farming* (1959); Stanford, J. K., *British Friesians, A History of the Breed* (1956); Thapar, Romila, *A History of India* (1966); Trist, P. J. O., *A Survey of the Agriculture of Suffolk* (1971); Trow-Smith, Robert, *British Livestock Husbandry to 1700* (1957), *British Livestock Husbandry, 1700–1900* (1959), *English Husbandry* (1961); Tallon, M. G., *La Réserve Zoologique et Botanique de Camargue* (1947); Whitestone, Linda, & Smith, Henry, *A Market in Animal Semen?* (1972); Whitlock, Ralph, *A Short History of Farming in Britain* (1965), *The Folklore of Wiltshire* (1976); Williams, Stephen, & Edgar, C. David *Planned Beef Production* (1966); Zeuner, F. E., *A History of Domesticated Animals* (1963).

Index

174

Tamarau, 22
Tankerville, Earl of, 29
Tassili, rock-paintings at *see* Jabbaren
Texas, U.S.A., 8

United States of America, 24; cattle breeding in, 111; cattle breeds of, 144, 145–6, 163–4, 165–6; destruction of bison in, 24–26, 25; ranching in, 88–90, 109, 122
Ur *see* Sumeria
Urus *see* Aurochs

Walton, Dr., 127
Wesley, John, 67
Weyhill, Hampshire, 44
Woolley, Sir Leonard, 46

Yak, 26, 27
Young, Arthur, 92, 94, 104

Zebu, 18–20, 111, 145, 163, 169–71, *opp. 161*
Zulu, cattle of, 19–20